First Steps

Basic Activities in the 3 Rs

Compiled by

D C Perkins, BA (Hons), MEd, PhD (Wales) and E J Perkins, BSc (Hons), MEd

Design & Illustrations Anthony James

Educational Adviser Alison John, BEd

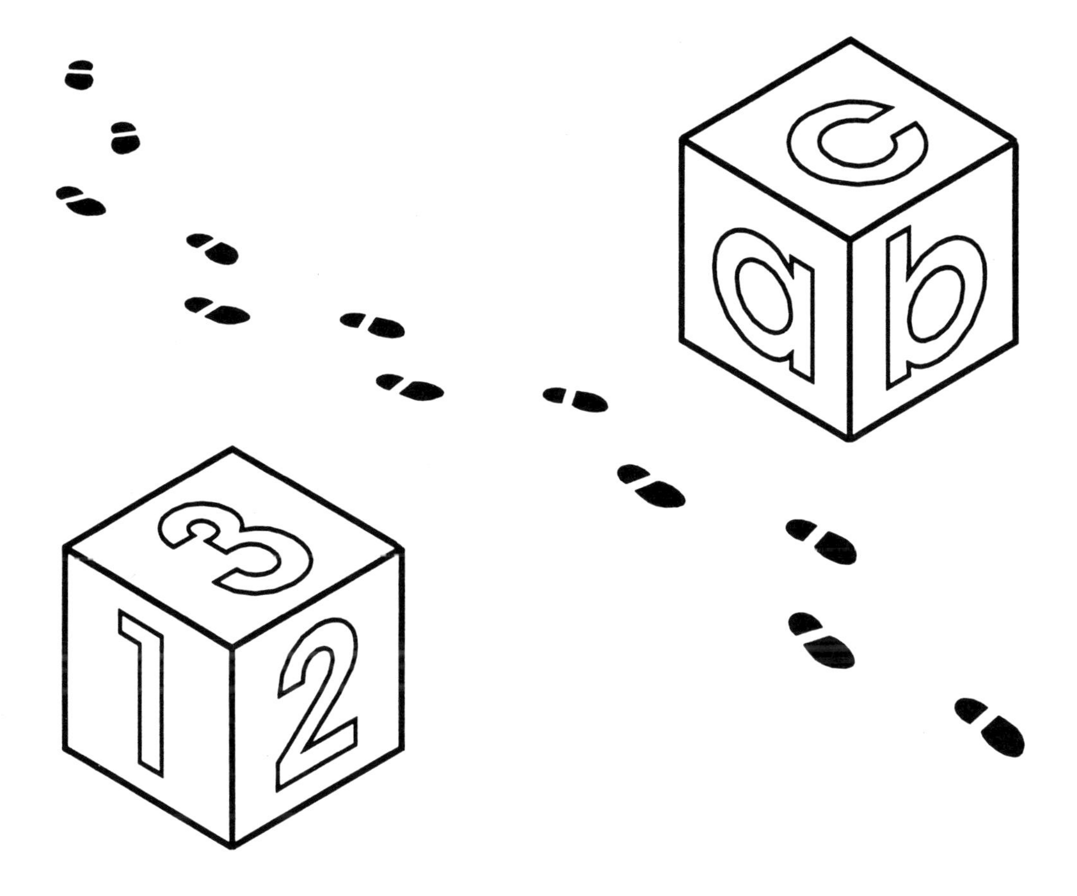

Domino Books (Wales) Ltd
Swansea SA1 1FN
Tel: 01792 459378 Fax: 01792 466337

ISBN 1 85772 130 6

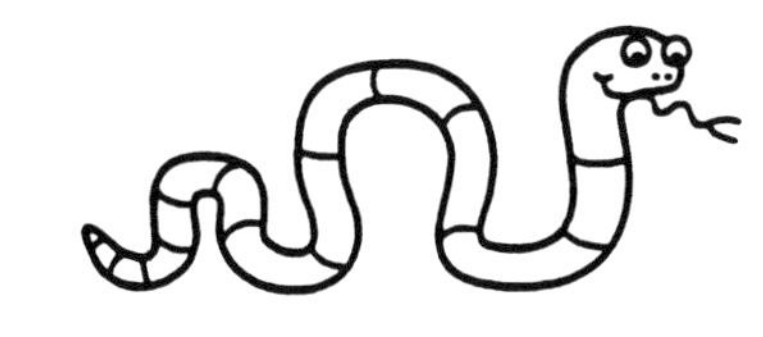

Contents

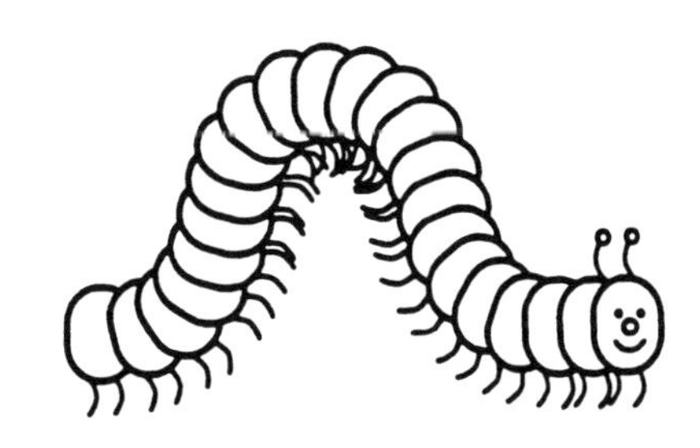

TEACHERS' NOTES

'FIRST STEPS' arose from a conversation with a group of teachers about the need for a book of photocopiable resources that could be used with very young children before formal teaching begins. This book is planned to be used with children under 5. Teachers of the over 5s are directed to the range of Master Files which have been prepared for children at Key Stage 1 of the National Curriculum.

Children begin to acquire language in their parents' arms. They learn to associate the human voice with the sensations of food, warmth and comfort. At first, language is a a means to an end and it is used by the young child to attract attention and to indicate what he or she wants: food, milk, love, warmth and so on. Nouns and verbs (the content words) are used first for they contain most meaning. The functional words: articles, prepositions, conjunctions come next and finally syntax and grammar (masculine and feminine, singulars and plurals, number and colour) come last. By the age of five, most children can be understood, they have basic (spoken) language acquisition.

Although the young child can make himself/herself understood, that is can speak the language, it does not mean that he/she is ready to proceed to learning the alphabet, the basis of written language. The aim of the teacher is bring the child to a situation where it is possible to master the alphabet.

At the outset five types of skill have to be developed:

1. **Motor skills,** i.e. skills related to movement. This includes manual dexterity.

2. **Visual perception,** i.e. skills related to seeing and awareness.

3. **Auditory perception,** i.e. skills related to hearing capabilities.

4. **Memory perception,** i.e. remembering what has been taught before.

5. **Social skills and relationships,** i.e. how to get on with other children.

For many experienced nursery teachers and carers the following few lines will seem superfluous. The activities in this book have been planned with the concepts underlying *Desirable Outcomes for Children's Learning* (SCAA) . Obviously, the ways in which the activities are used depends on the age, ability and experience of the children and the resources available. We do not envisage any problems choosing appropriate material.

1. All the material in this book is photocopiable as defined on the first page. This means that all the material can be used in any way you wish. Drawings can be photocopied and adapted for further work.

2. Covering sections of the master copies with plain paper enables resource material to be used in different ways. This is useful when it is felt that the material on one sheet should be used at different times especially with children who are slower at learning.

3. The master copies can be enlarged to A3 making it easier for several children to work on them at the same time.

4. Some of the photocopies can be cut to make additional puzzles and games.

5. It is intended that the material should be used selectively depending on the ages and abilities of the children.

6. Much of the completed work may be used as visual aids around the classroom.
   Children feel pride when their work is 'pinned up'. It is important that each child's work should be 'exhibited' as often as possible. As well as encouraging them to produce their best, presentation of work in this way enables parents to keep in touch with what is happening and to assess the progress of their children.

7. Remember, there are often several ways in which problems can be tackled. Suggestions from children and the exchange of ideas should be encouraged. Learning to put forward ideas and to listen to the ideas of others are invaluable skills. Encourage the development of leaders but make sure that all take part. Some children are reticent about putting forward their ideas or answering questions. An incorrect answer can be often be useful because it shows how material has been understood or mis-understood by the children. Children have to learn that it is OK to be wrong and not to be worried about this. Build confidence wherever possible although praise must be justifiable.

8. Learning to work on their own or in groups now enables children to cope with the move to primary school later. Leadership and teamwork skills may develop at a very young age and will be invaluable throughout life.

9. Activities leading to logical thinking are invaluable. Teaching children to question material presented to them, to plan their work, to hypothesise and then to test their theories are skills that will help them in their everyday work when they are grown up: good habits learned now will last.

10. Learning is about discoveries and adventures, above all it should be fun: never boring and never dull.

It is very important to keep the activities within the ability and the stage of development of the individual child. Moving too fast, unintentionally trying to do too much or extending the material too far cause confusion and fear. As well, we have all met the bright child who becomes bored and frustrated because he/she is not able to go fast enough. No one said teaching was easy.

SHAPES

The basic aim of these activities is to help the children recognise the different shapes. It is helpful to outline the shapes using rolls of Plasticine. The activities help the children to identify and recognize similarities and differences between the shapes. They help to develop general perception skills which are needed for reading for meaning when a child picks out essential information from complex material. Many similar shapes are of different sizes and these can be used to develop the child's skills of comparison. The idea of sets is an important mathematical concept that objects can be classified together by shape, colour or another parameter.

CIRCLES Begin by talking about circles in the classroom - clock and toys. Ask the children what they know about circles in their homes and elsewhere - bikes, cars, buses ... If it enters the conversation with the class, mention wheels and association with movement.

Page 2 Encourage the children to trace the circles with their fingers (tracking). Then the children can use coloured crayons. Describe a circle using words such as round, roundabout, ring, hoop. Photocopy the sheet, cut out the circles and match them with the circles on another copy. Let the children colour the circles and make patterns from them.

Page 3 Very familiar circles. The children should name the objects and say where they are likely to find them.

Page 4 Practice in drawing circles. The children should name the objects. If possible they should say what each circle does. The children should draw their own pictures using circles.

Page 5 An exercise in picking out circles. Discuss what clowns do and why they make people laugh.

Reinforce these activities on circles by class games played in circles: ring a ring a rosies, pass the parcel, passing a message by whispering (in a circle), odd man out (with child in the centre of a circle) and action rhymes.

SQUARES Begin by talking about squares in the classroom - windows, books, blackboard, toys ... Ask the children about squares in their homes and elsewhere - televisions, computers, washing machines, pictures, electrical switches, boxes ...

Page 6 Encourage the children to trace the squares with their fingers (tracking). Then the children can use coloured crayons. Describe a square using words such as side, flat. Photocopy the sheet, cut out the squares and match them with the squares on another copy. Let the children colour the squares and make patterns from them.

Page 7 Squares to pick out and colour.

Page 8 Practice in drawing squares. The children should name the objects and say what each square does.

Page 9 An exercise in picking out squares. The children should name the objects and say where they are likely to find them. They can trace the squares with their fingers before colouring the pictures.

Let the children form squares, that is stand in squares with the same number of children making each side.
Look at crosswords, check patterns and boards for games especially draughts.

TRIANGLES Begin by talking about triangles - tepees, hats, flags, kites, cones ... Ask the children what they know about triangles.

Page 10 Encourage the children to trace the triangles with their fingers (tracking). Then the children can use crayons to colour the triangles. Describe a triangle using words such as side, three. Photocopy the sheet, cut out the triangles and match them with the triangles on another copy. Let the children colour the triangles and make patterns from them.

Page 11 The children should name the objects and say where they are likely to find them.

Page 12 Practice in drawing triangles. The children should name the objects. If possible they should say what each triangle does. The children should draw their own pictures using triangles.

Page 13 An exercise in picking out triangles. The children should name all the objects and colour the triangles.

Bring a musical triangle to school and have the children take turns to play it.

RECTANGLES Begin by talking about rectangles in the classroom - windows, doors, envelopes, rulers ... Ask the children about rectangles in their homes and elsewhere.

Page 14 Encourage the children to trace the rectangles with their fingers (tracking). Then the children can use crayons to colour the rectangles. Describe a rectangle using words such as side, flat. Photocopy the sheet, cut out the rectangles and match them with the rectangles on another copy. Let the children colour the rectangles and make patterns from them.

Page 15 The children should name the objects and say where they are likely to find them.

Page 16 Practice in drawing rectangles. The children should name the objects. If possible they should say what each rectangle does. The children should draw their own pictures using rectangles.

Page 17 An exercise in picking out rectangles. The children should name all the objects and colour the rectangles.

Use all friezes and pictures as well as a display table or desk to reinforce shapes.

Reinforce these activities by cutting out the different shapes from the photocopies and test whether the children can recognise each one. Mix them up and let the children sort them out (into sets). Hold up the shapes on large cards and ask the children to recognise them. Make domino cards using the shapes.

When the children have developed their skills sufficiently, let the children colour the shapes and cut them out, then mix them. The shapes can then be sorted in different ways: into sets of similar shapes or of similar colours.

The same shapes are of different sizes and can also be used as examples of bigger, smaller, smallest ...

NUMBER and COUNTING

Desirable Outcomes for Children's Learning (SCAA) require that children should

recognise and use numbers to ten.

become familiar with larger numbers from everyday life.

have experience in solving practical problems.

learn to record numbers.

have experience in using number operations.

develop the language of number.

Early operations such as addition and subtraction which young children already experience in everyday life should be developed through nursery activities. The giving out of biscuits or cakes or drinks involves the concepts of enough, more, fewer ... Children will also be aware of sharing (practical dividing) but formal concepts are not appropriate.

In their everyday experiences, children see numbers that are much larger than those usually dealt with in the nursery. Role play encourages children to become familiar with quantities used in real life.

Young children can recognise small quantities of one, two and three but are confused by large numbers. Children's ability to recognise a small quantity and name how many is called subitizing. Thus, by the time children start nursery education at 3 or 4, they may already have acquired some understanding of number. They may

be able to recognise and name small quantities.

be able to appreciate that one group can have more or less than another or have the same quantity.

know some number tags/labels but not say them in the correct order.

apply a number tag to each item as they count (but not necessarily in the correct order).

Although children may learn to recite numbers in the correct order, it does not mean that they can count out a certain number of objects.

Children need to learn to recite the counting words in the correct order.

They should touch and count each item only once. They may find it helpful to move the counted objects into a pile separate from those which have not been counted or to mark the item with a dot or tick as it is counted. Children find it easier to count items arranged in a line rather than scattered randomly.

The touch/moving/marking should be at the same time as the count word is said.

Children often touch the same item twice, miss an item, repeat the same counting name, miss out a counting name or do not co-ordinate touching and counting.

Children may record a number on paper as a pictogram, an iconic recording or with a symbol.

PROBLEM SOLVING

Much of the work during nursery involves solving problems. Some may be dealt with in a short time others may take a few days.

1. Starting a task involves understanding the problem and deciding what to do.
2. Carrying out the task may mean choosing ways and means, deciding on materials, drawing a picture and trying out different strategies to find out one that works.
3. Reporting on the task and discussing the results and other possible ways of carrying it out.

These three stages involved in problem solving match those in Key Stage 1, Using and Applying Mathematics of the English Mathematics National Curriculum, that is

1. Making and monitoring decisions to solve problems.
2. Developing mathematical language and communication.
3. Developing mathematical reasoning.

Some of the skills associated with the National Curriculum are appropriate with younger children.

Making a plan This will be verbal but children can be encouraged to draw a picture and record numbers in whatever way they choose.

Choosing materials This may have already been decided by the nature of the problem. If not then the children can discuss and decide what is best.

Estimating Children should be encouraged to make a guess and then if possible find out how close they are by counting.

Use knowledge they have already acquired.

Discuss the progress of the task. Learning to evaluate how a task is getting on is an invaluable skill.

Evaluating the effectiveness of the work. The final work should be compared with what was planned at the outset. Learning to put forward ideas and opinions and at the same time listen to other people is an important part of education.

Throughout, children should be encouraged to try and tackle problems, suggest alternative strategies, persevere even when the going becomes difficult, learn to work with their peers and be willing to put forward and to listen to other opinions and solutions.

Ordering Children need to know the language of ordering: first, second, third ...

Addition and subtraction Children should understand that N+1 is more than N and that N-1 is less than N. Use finger counting and encourage children to make estimates of small quantities. They should understand zero.

Division, fractions and multiplication Discuss sharing out.

Large numbers These can be recoginised in context such as telephone numbers, car numbers and house numbers.

Recording Use pictographic, iconic or symbolic responses. A number frieze, clearly displayed, gives children a point of reference for identifying numbers. They need not be displayed on the wall but can consist, for example, of different numbers of objects put in a jar with the appropriate numeral on the outside.

Experience of ordering, using number operations, larger numerals, recording and solving problems using number can be part of nursery work.

Numeral displays should include numerals for small and big numbers such as telephone numbers, number plates.

Books, rhymes and songs There are many action stories, rhymes and songs which are useful. Some examples are included in this book.

Cooking At home children love to help in the kitchen and cooking contains all the concepts of mathematics and the associated language. Role play in the nursery is invaluable in this kind of activity.

The activities in this book introduce the concepts associated with the shape of the numbers, identifying the quantity or number of objects, linking a number to quantity, reading word and number and using colour to distinguish different quantities.

Pages 26 - 51 Children should track the number on each page and colour the numbers. They can make the numbers out of rolls of Plasticine then follow the guidelines and write the numbers themselves. They can count the objects on each page, touch each one and mark each with a dot or a tick.

Pages 26 - 35 Exercises in number recognition and counting.

Pages 36 - 45 Exercises in sorting different items, counting them and matching the totals to the correct numbers.

Page 46 Joining dots in the correct number order is always enjoyed by children and the completed pictures can be coloured.

Pages 47 - 51 These exercises reinforce matching on a one-to-one level as well as developing dexterity.

LANGUAGE, RHYME AND MEMORY

LISTENING

Language learning embodies listening, speaking, reading and writing skills. For very young children the first two skills are paramount. They have to be taught to listen attentively. Tell them stories and when you repeat a story get them to take part. Nursery rhymes are in a sense stories in miniature. Say these to the children and let them repeat them to emphasize the rhyme and rhythm. If possible, let the children tap the table in front of them or clap their hands to the 'beat of the rhyme'. Use the well known nursery rhymes at first with pictures to pinpoint the 'story' elements. e.g.

Little Miss Muffet
Sat on a tuffet
Eating her curds and whey;
There came a big spider
Who sat down beside her
And frightened Miss Muffet away.

Words like *tuffet, curds* and *whey* would have to be explained but the main story line is the fear of the spider. Enquire about the children's attitude to crawly creatures: some of the older children may have seen the film *Arachnaphobia.*

Whenever possible illustrate simple rhymes with your fingers and get the children to follow your example. Remember that very young children will not be as dextrous as you are but even they should be able to manage exercises like the following:

Five little soldiers
Standing in a row,
Three stood straight
And two stood so.
Along came the General
And what do you think?
Up jumped those soldiers
As quick as a wink.

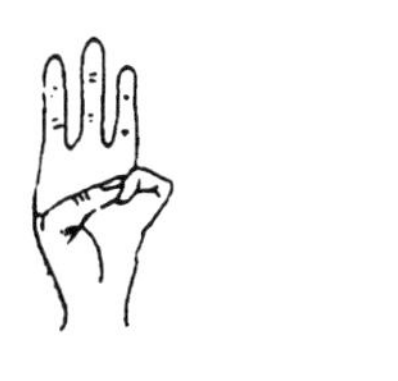

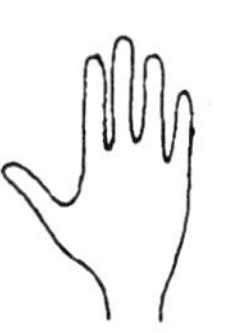

Note the story element: the soldiers, the approach of the general, the need for them to stand to attention, the discipline and remember the importance of numbers - five, three and two. This can also be acted out and enjoyed by the children. (Also *standing in a row* and *quick as a wink.*)

Stories fascinate young children and read them as often as you can. They widen the child's world and fire the imagination. A few traditional favourites are illustrated in this book: *Goldilocks and the Three Bears, Little Red Riding Hood* and *The Three Little Pigs.* Encourage the children to take an active part. After they have become familiar with a story get them to tell it to you and use role play as often as possible. Extra fun is provided if you allow the children to dress up as they are acting the parts. It is important to get parents to help with the development of these listening techniques. Stories, especially at bedtime, are important experiences for the young child and often tempt reluctant sleepyheads to go to bed. Traditional tales (see page 9) are useful starters.

SPEAKING

We have already mentioned the importance of getting the children to participate and this will give them speaking practice. Whenever possible, let them combine speaking with actions. Repetition is important and as far as the children are concerned, **familiarity** is an important factor in all their activities. Rhymes and songs need to be spoken and sung time and again and the children will soon know them by heart. (If you change a word the children are delighted to point out your 'mistake'.) Speaking and actions, e.g. *Ten Little Men,* should be repeated as well as short rhymes like *I'm a little teapot, short and stout.* Use the game *Simon says* to promote action work. Much of the speaking in these early years is in response to questions but whenever possible encourage them to talk about their homes, families, holidays and pastimes and anything else which interests them.

RHYME The importance of rhyme and rhythm for very young children cannot be overestimated. First, let them listen to rhyme and rhythm and then get them to participate. If possible give the children something to use in these 'poetry' activities such as a bell, triangle, drum, tambourine, maracas or whistle. These can be blown or shaken in time with the beat with you leading. A list of suggested rhymes is given at the end of this section.

MEMORY WORK

We have already mentioned memory work and many of the rhymes and stories will soon be remembered by the children. To develop the children's memories further devise activities like the following:

Treasure Hunt Hide a variety of small articles around the classroom. Let the children hunt for them in groups or

pairs. Give the children cards on which the prizes are drawn and written. Use 'hot' and 'cold' instructions if this helps - it usually adds to the excitement.
Memory Tray Place a variety of different objects on a tray and let the children look at them for a few minutes. Ask the children to remember the items then cover the tray with a piece of paper and ask them to say what they saw. Next remove one of the objects (without the children seeing which one) and ask them what is missing. The photocopiable master Memory Time in this book illustrates this activity.
Another activity involves pictures of familiar objects cut from a book. Remove part of an object such as a tail, a ear or a leg. Ask the children what is missing. If drawings are used, ask the children to complete them.

PRE-READING SKILLS -MATCHING AND SEQUENCING
Several of the photocopiable masters are designed to help the children develop their basic reasoning capabilities and visual awareness of shape and detail. There are also those which require picture sequencing, e.g. the sheets on *Humpty Dumpty, Goldilocks, Little Red Riding Hood* and *The Three Little Pigs.* These are planned to help the children to read pictures to find out what is happening in a story. They are also useful because they give them confidence to look at the words that go with the pictures. Matching requires them to recognise like with like and to distinguish shapes, drawings, numbers and letters which are different. Sequencing helps children to put events in a logical order. At a later stage the children will be expected to sequence nursery rhymes and simple stories including non-fiction material.

PRE-WRITING SKILLS
Sequencing and matching are important as a basis for writing later on. For example, adding tails to animals, colouring and tracing activities, cutting and pasting are part of the early development of these important skills. Teach the children to hold crayons and pencils properly.

LEFT AND RIGHT, UP AND DOWN, BACKWARDS AND FORWARDS
Putting pictures in the appropriate order helps to reinforce the left to right, up and down and backwards and forwards orientation. For left and right orientation, use the *I'm a Teapot* photocopiable master as a basic tool and follow this by the Hokey Cokey if possible.

Give verbal instructions to reinforce all these movements. For example,

Hold up your right hand.
Bend your left knee.
Touch your right eye.
Touch your toes.
Tap your head.
Look up.
Look down.
Walk forwards to me.
Walk backwards to your desk.

GAMES
Elsewhere we have stressed the importance of play at this age. Whenever possible, use the play elements in the photocopiable masters in this book. If the children are divided into two groups or sets, a competitive element is introduced and this can be fun. The sets should be equitable and avoid boys only and girls only groups. Games include I spy, Hunt the thimble, Simon says, Pass the parcel, Blind man's buff, Sticking the tail on a donkey, Hide and seek, musical chairs, Musical bumps, Statues, Ring a ring a rosies ... Miming actions are very useful, e.g. reading a book/ newspaper, threading a needle, wrapping a parcel, feeding the dog, using a telephone, driving a car ... This leads to What's my line and charades. Most important of all is role play and there is plenty of scope for this using poetry and prose.

THE ALPHABET

Young children find the alphabet difficult. Lower case letters give words distinctive shapes while capital letters do not. Do not teach the alphabet too soon. The letters need to be reinforced by all the methods you know. Let the children colour the drawings in the photocopiable masters and say the letters and words. The sheets can be photocopied, enlarged or laminated. Let the children cut out the letters and paste them in their books. The last sheet may be used for alphabet lotto and alphabet snap.

STORIES AND RHYMES

STORIES
Aladdin
Beauty and the Beast
Beddgelert
Charlie and the Chocolate Factory
Cinderella
Goldilocks and the Three Bears
Gulliver's Travels
Hansel and Gretel
Jack and the Beanstalk
James and the Giant Peach
Little Red Riding Hood
Rumplestiltskin
Pinocchio
Puss in Boots
Rapunzel
Ricki Tikki Tavi
Robin Hood
SleepingBeauty
Snow White
The Cat and the Fox
The Hare and the Tortoise
The Princess and the Pea
The Three Billy Goats Gruff
The Three Little Pigs
The Ugly Duckling
Thumbelina

NURSERY RHYMES
As I was going to St Ives
Baa Baa Black Sheep
Ding Dong Dell
Gcorgic Porgie
Hey Diddle Diddle
Hickory, Dickory, Dock
Humpty Dumpty
Hush-a-Bye, Baby
Jack and Jill
Little Bo-Peep
Mary Had a Little Lamb
Monday's Child
Old King Cole
One, Two, Buckle My Shoe
Oh Dear, What Can the Matter Be?
Oh, the Brave Old Duke of York
Polly, Put the Kettle On
Pop Goes the Weasel
Sing a Song of Sixpence
The First Day of Christmas
The North Wind Does Blow
There was a Crooked Man
There was an Old Woman Who Lived in a Shoe
Three Blind Mice
Twinkle, Twinkle, Little Star

ACTION RHYMES
Here We Go Looby Loo
Here We Go Round the Mulberry Bush
Old Macdonald Had a Farm
One, Two, Buckle My Shoe
One, Two, Three, Four, Five,
Once I Caught a Fish Alive
One, Two, Three, Four, Mary at the Cottage Door
Oranges and Lemons
Ring-a-Ring a'Roses
Ten Green Bottles
The Farmer's in His Den
This is the Way We Wash Our Face
Two Little Dicky Birds

FINGER PLAY RHYMES
Church and Steeple
Five Fat Gentlemen
Five Little Soldiers
Here's the Lady's Knives and Forks
I Am a Teapot
Peter Hammers with One Hammer
Incy Wincy Spider
Ten Little Men
Two Little Dicky Birds

TONGUE TWISTERS
Fuzzy Wuzzy Was a Bear
How Much Wood Would a Woodchuck Chuck
Peter Piper Picked a Peck of Pickled Pepper
She Sells Sea Shells on the Sea Shore

Circles

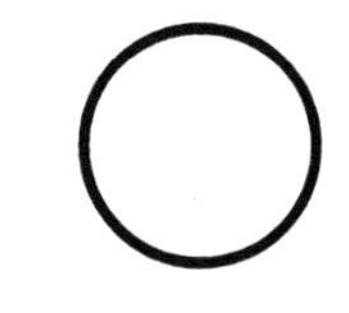

Colour the circles and cut them out.

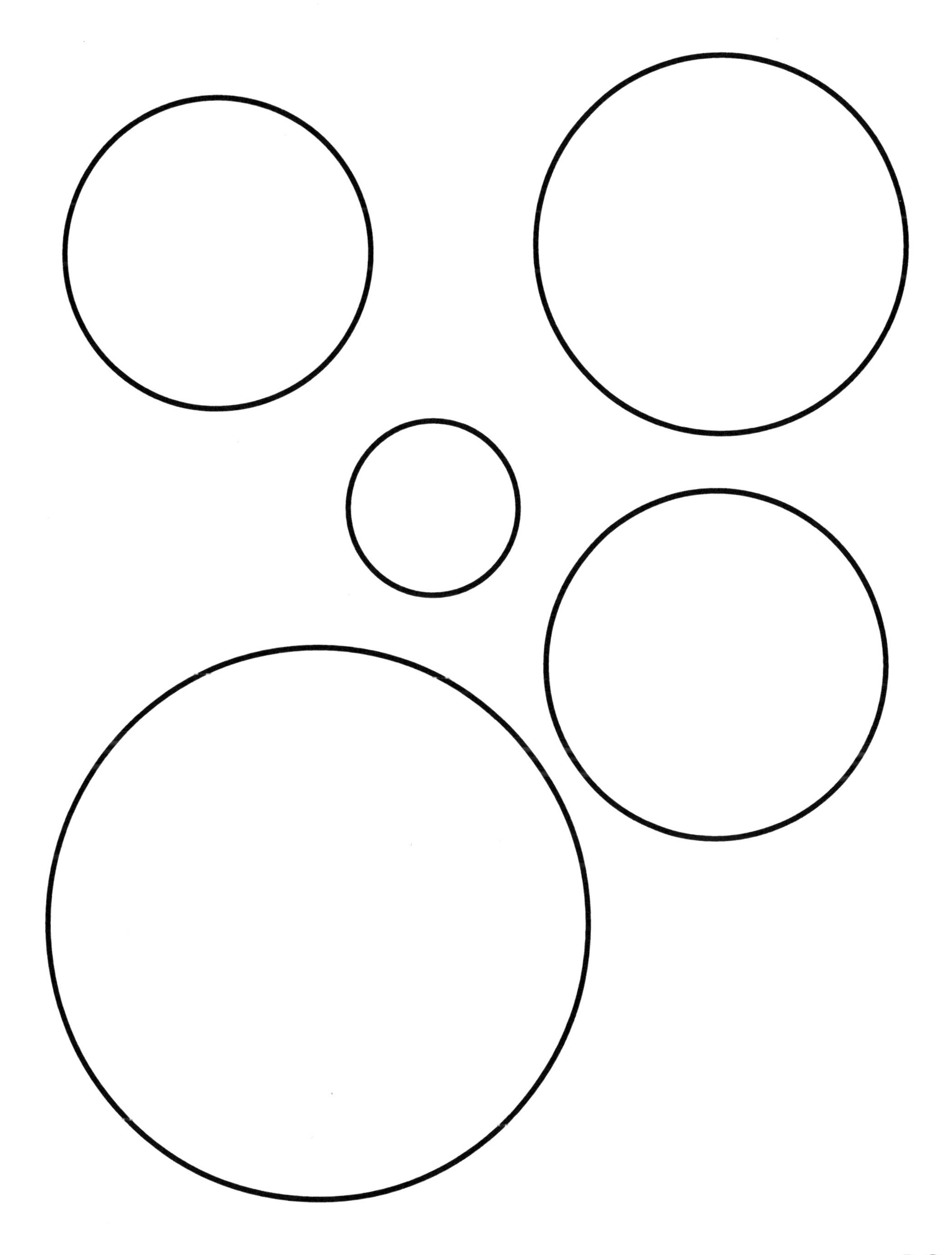

Circles

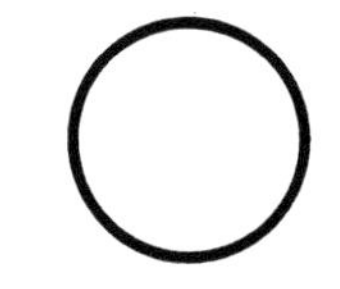

Look carefully at these pictures.
Colour the circles.

Circles

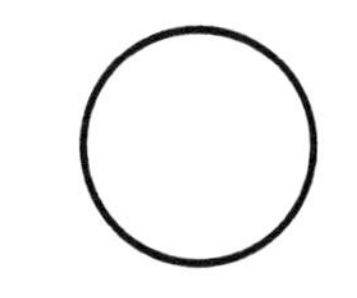

Join the dots to draw the missing circles.

Circles

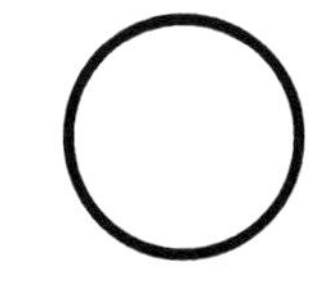

Colour the circles on the clown.

Squares

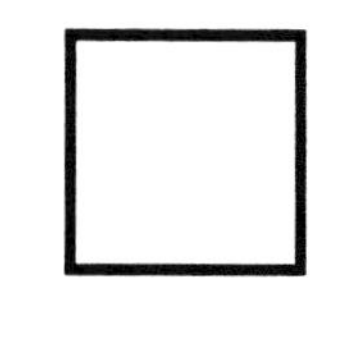

Colour the squares and cut them out.

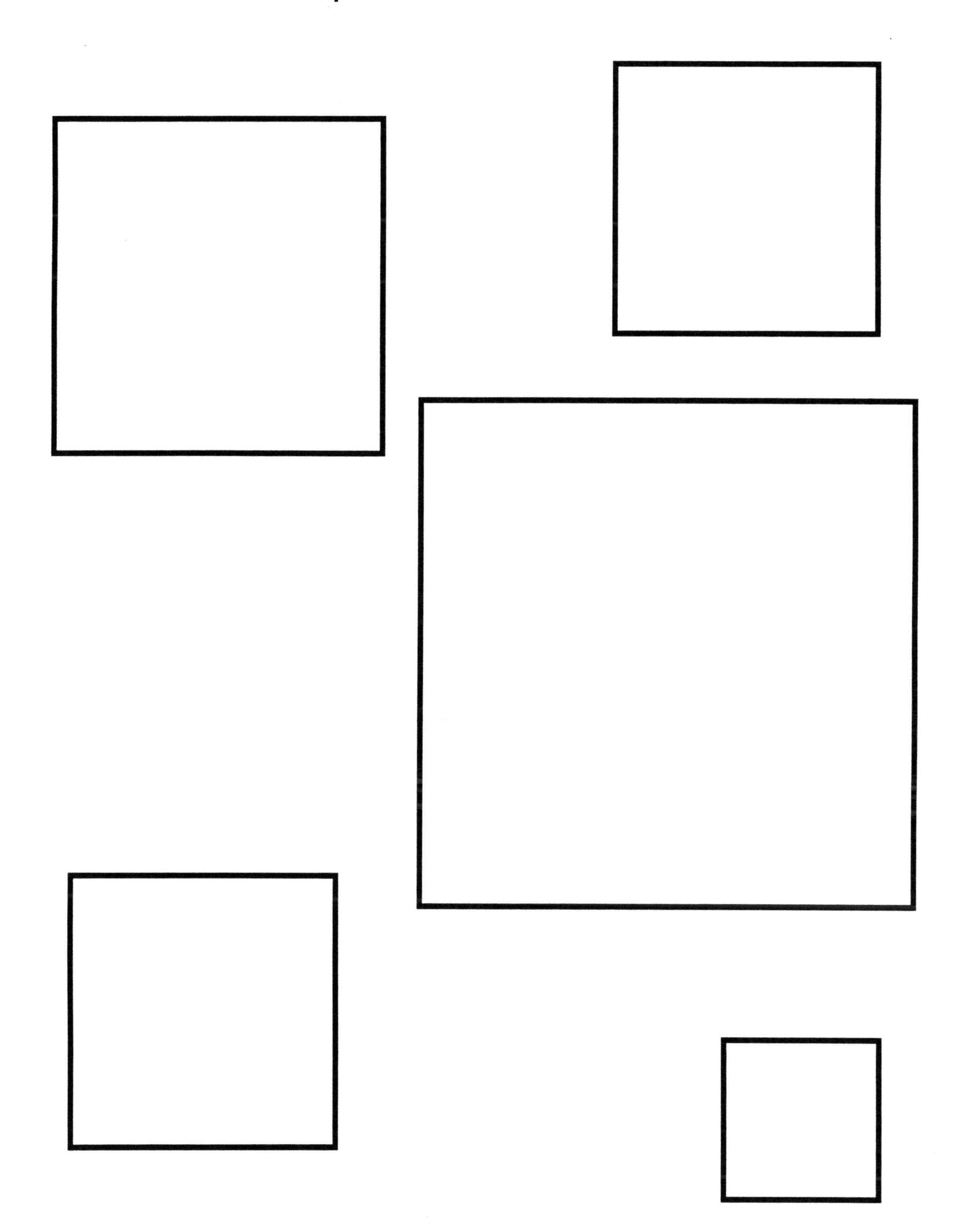

Squares

Look carefully at these pictures.
Colour the squares.

Squares

Join the dots to draw the missing squares.

Squares

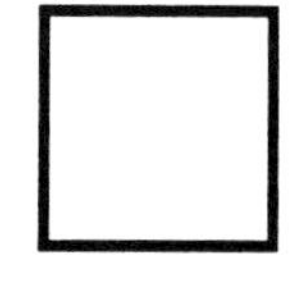

Colour the squares on the house.

Triangles

Colour the triangles and cut them out.

Triangles

Look carefully at these pictures.
Colour the triangles.

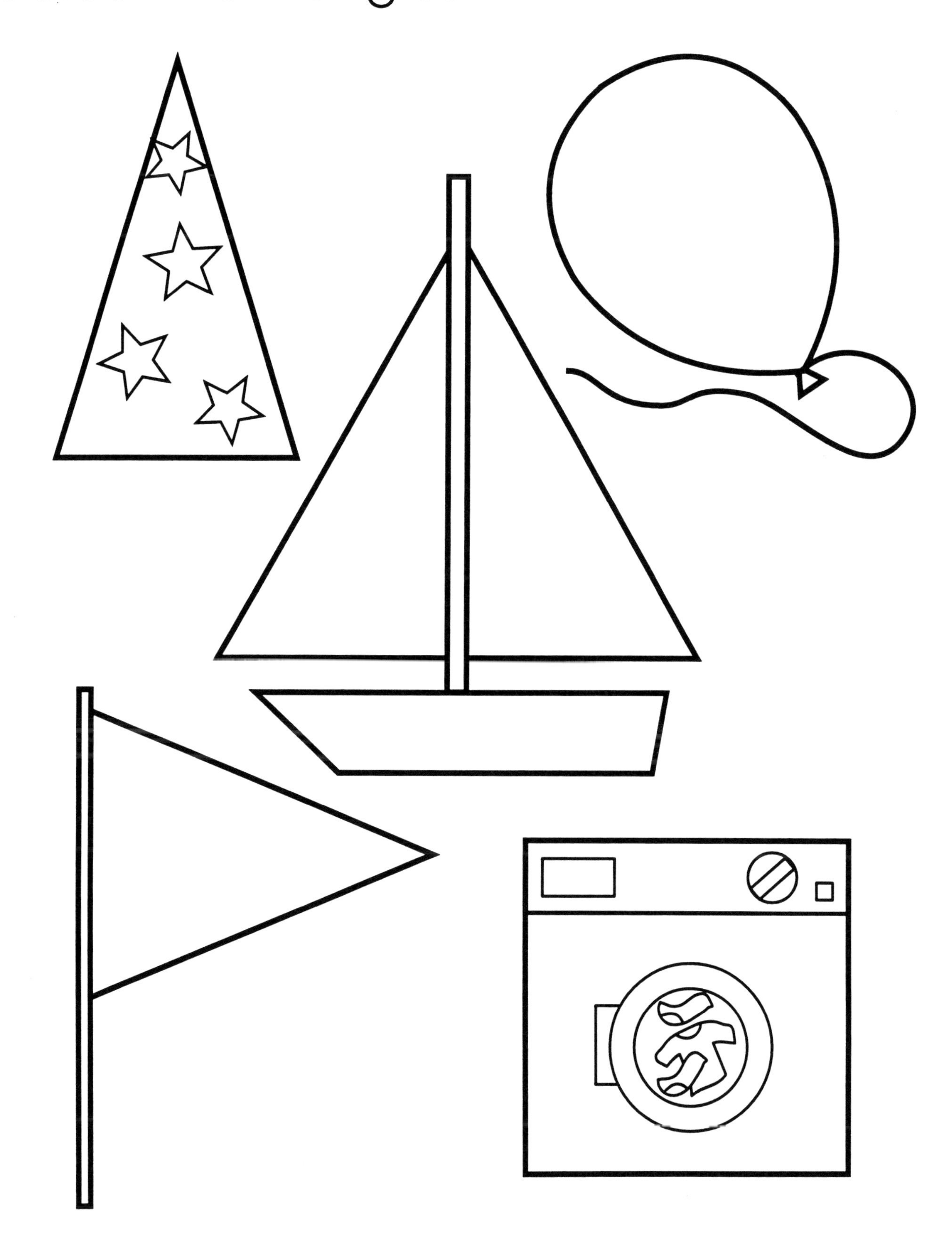

Triangles

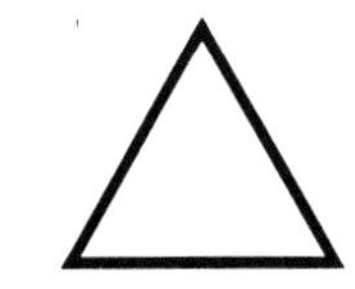

Join the dots to draw the missing triangles.

Triangles

Colour the triangles on the rocket.

Rectangles

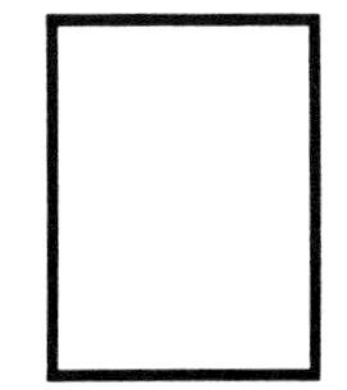

Colour the rectangles and cut them out.

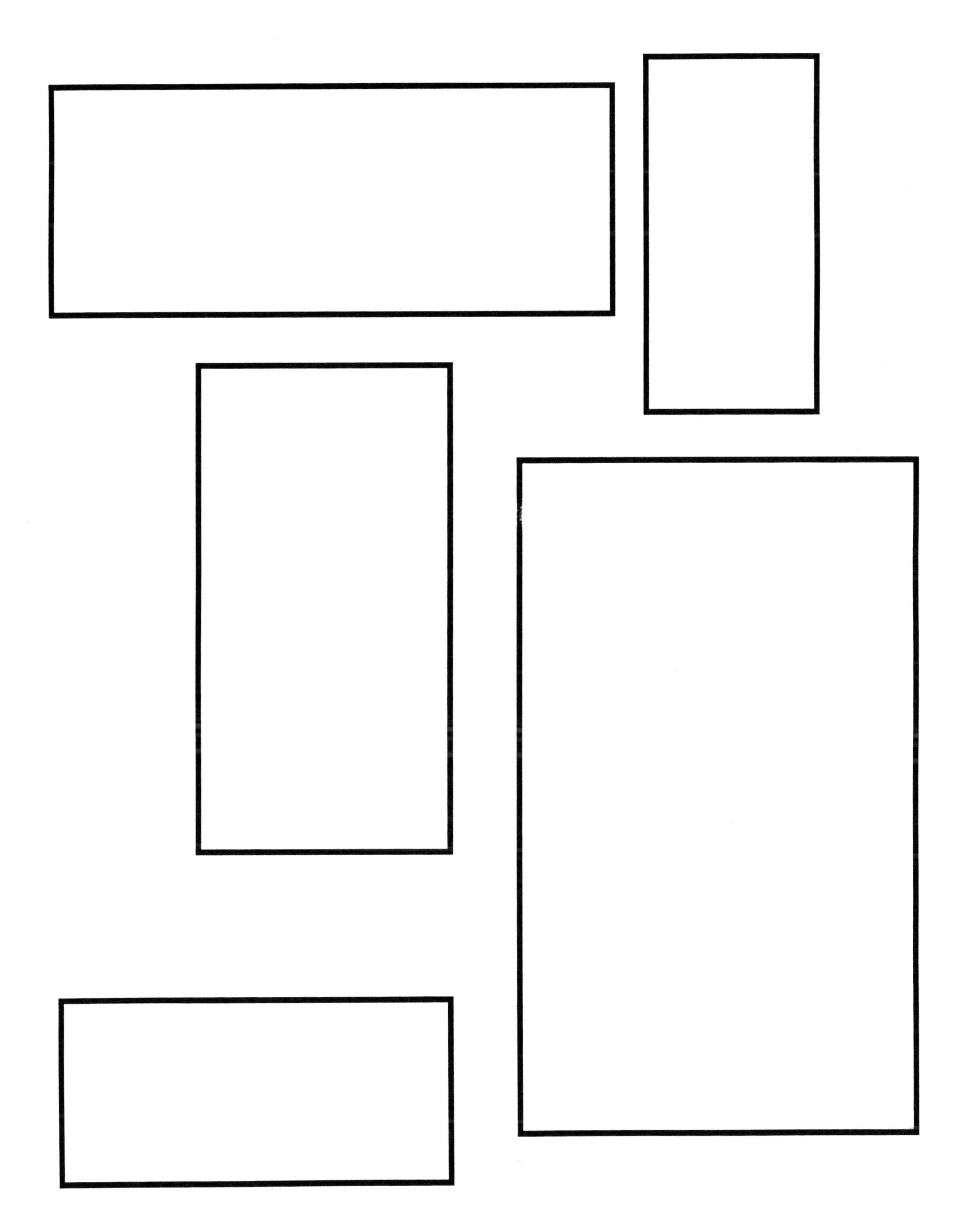

Rectangles

Look carefully at these pictures.
Colour the rectangles.

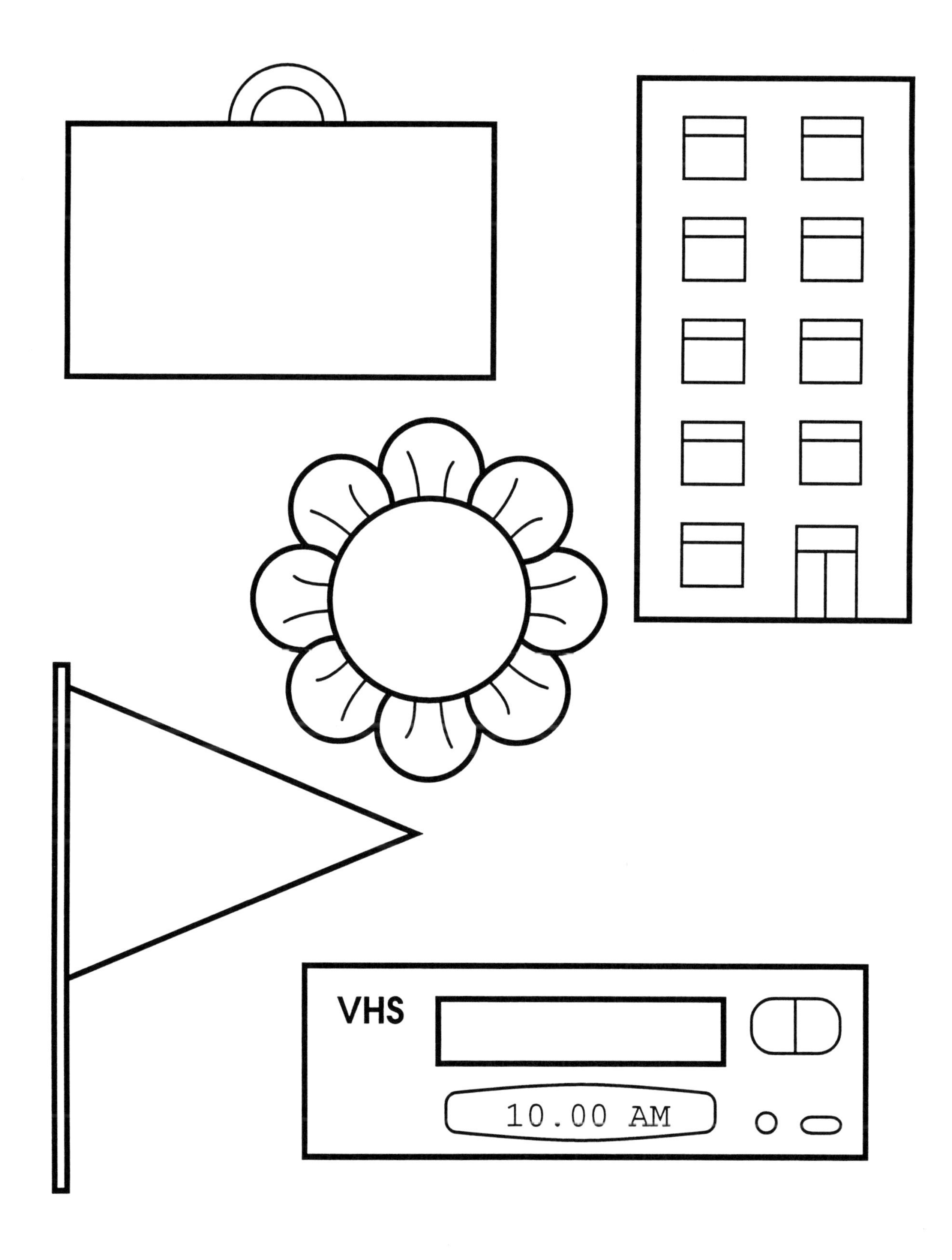

Rectangles

Join the dots to draw the missing rectangles.

Rectangles

Colour the rectangles on the ship.

1
one

2
two
2 2 2 2

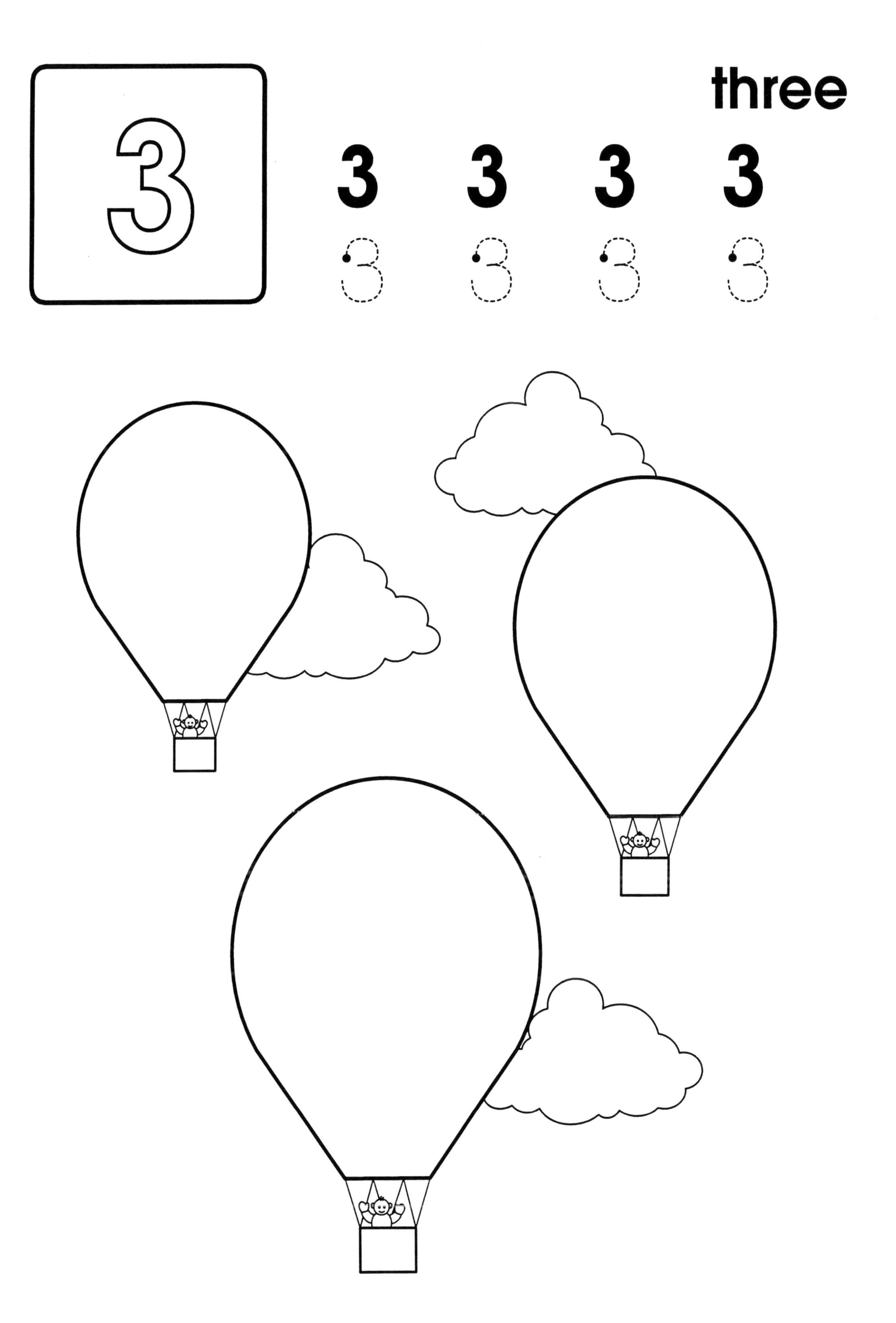
3
three
3 3 3 3

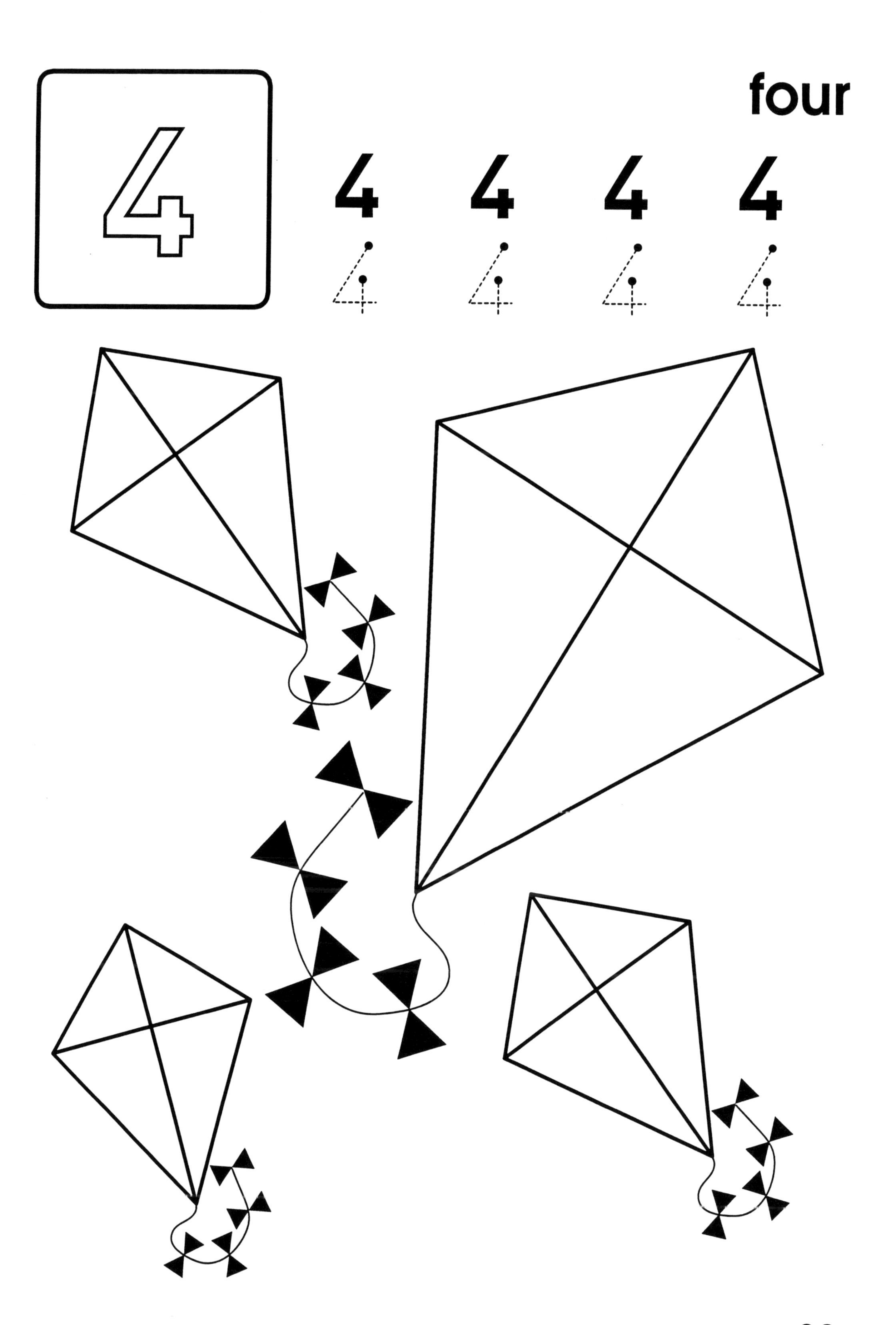
4
four
4 4 4 4

5
five
5 5 5 5

6
six
6 6 6 6

7
seven
7 7 7 7

8
eight
8 8 8 8

q
nine
q q q q

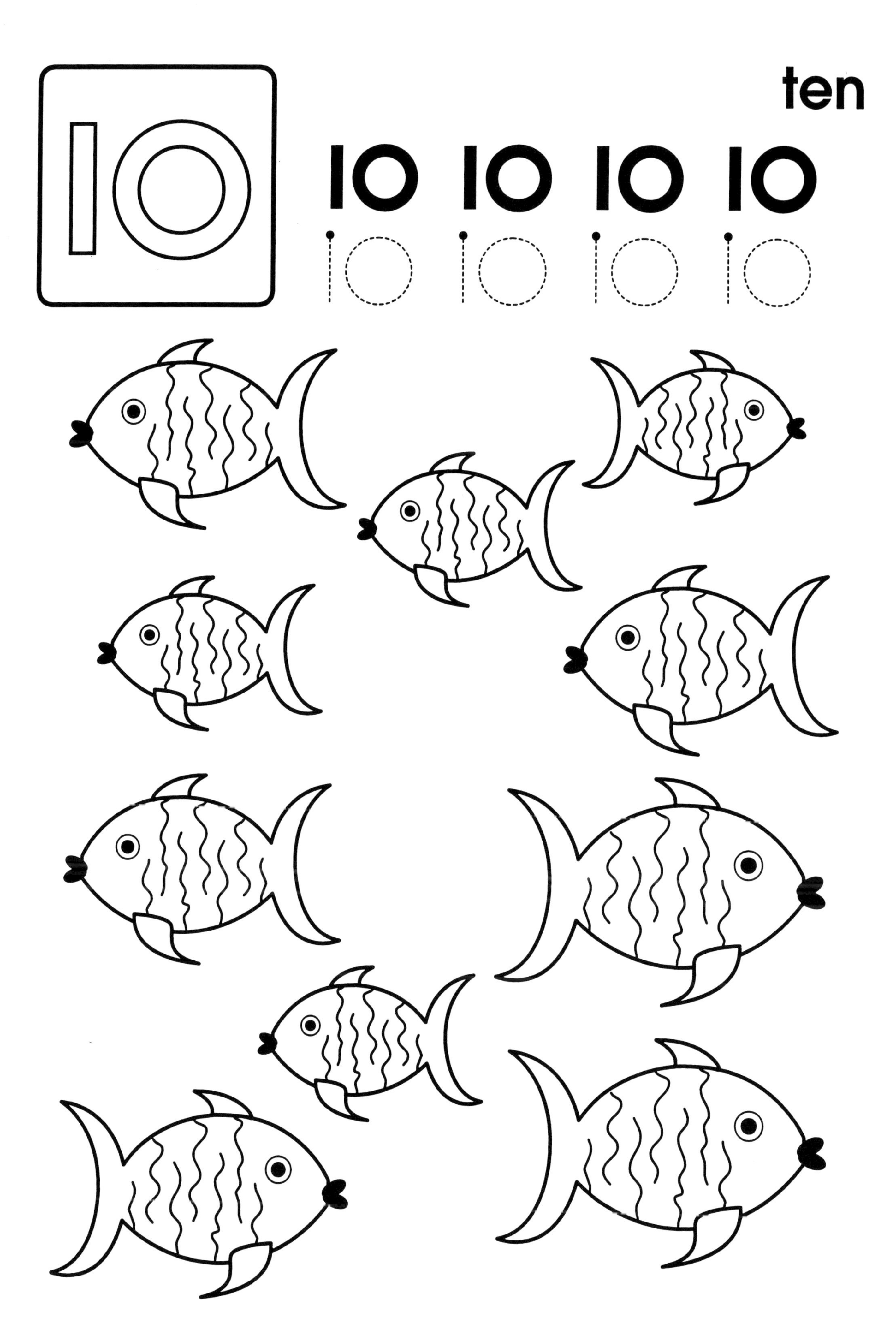
ten
10 10 10 10 10

Cut out the numbers. Paste them in the boxes.

1	2	3	4	5

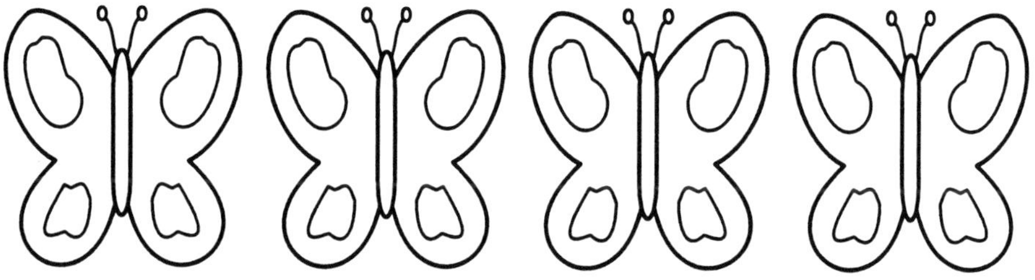

Cut out the numbers. Paste them in the boxes.

Draw a line to join the number to the picture.

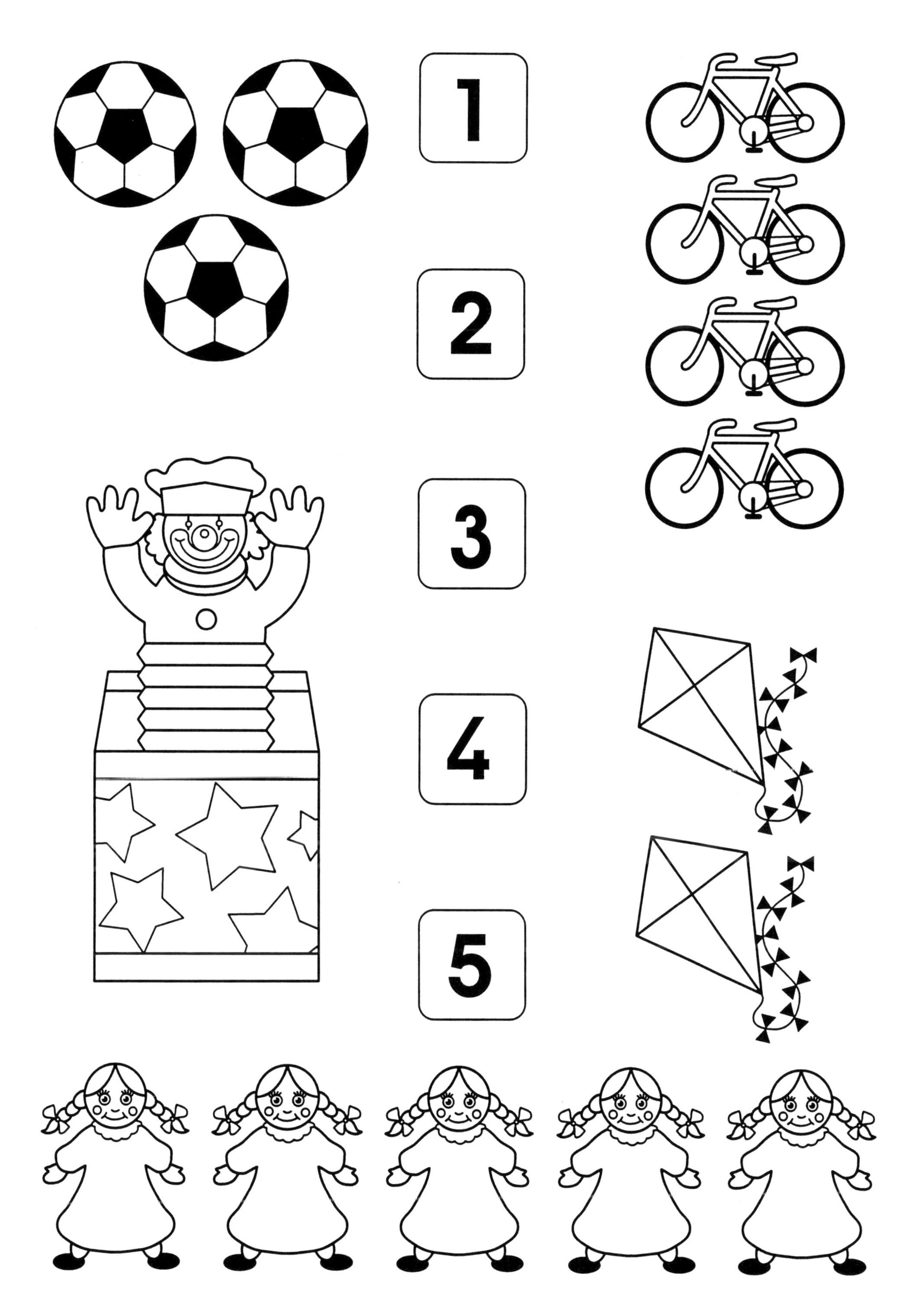

Draw a line to join the number to the picture.

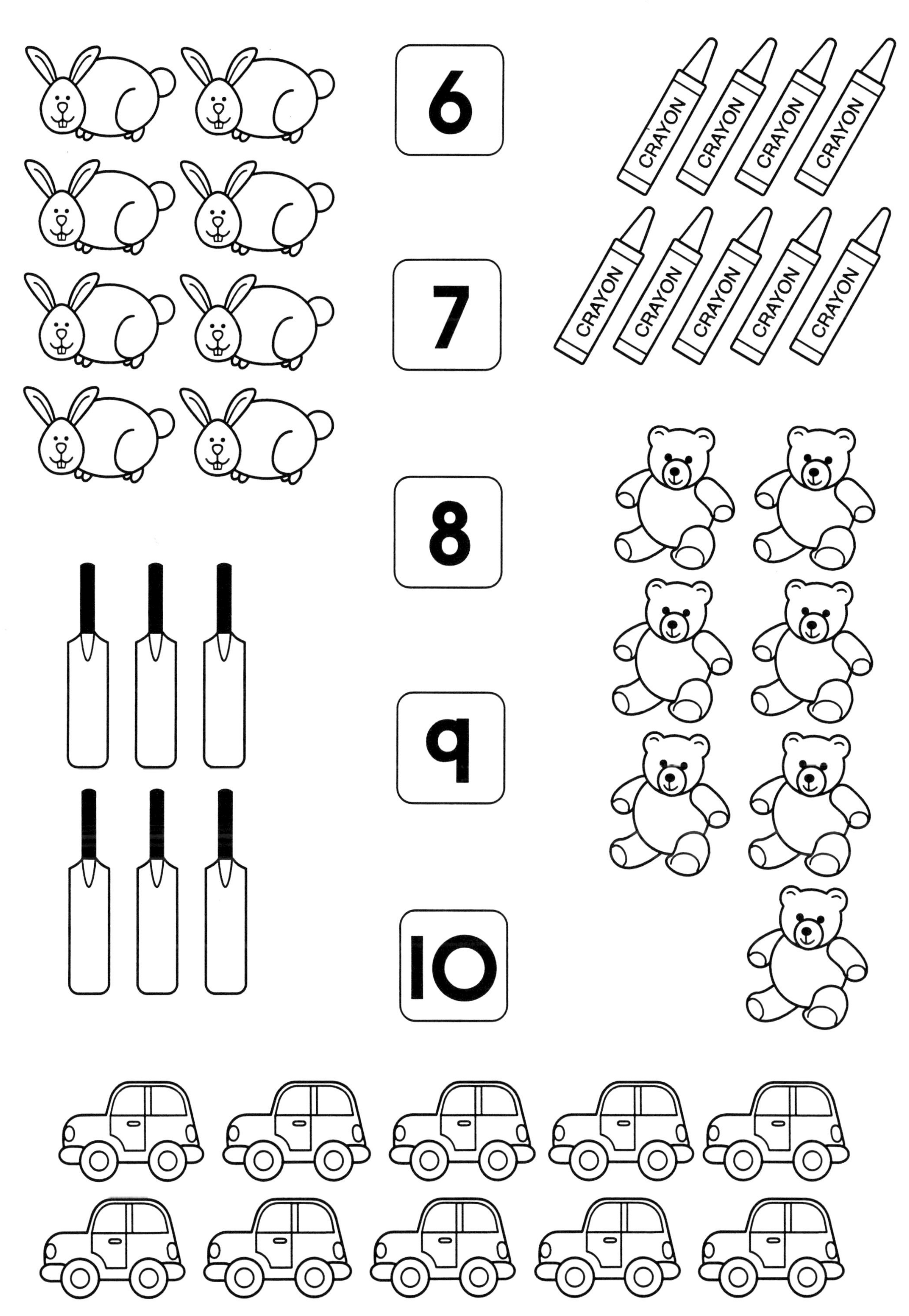

1 2 3 4 5 6 7 8 9 10

1 2 3 4 5 6 7 8 9 10

Write the numbers in the squares.

On the farm

1 2 3 4 5 6 7 8 9 10

Circle the numbers.

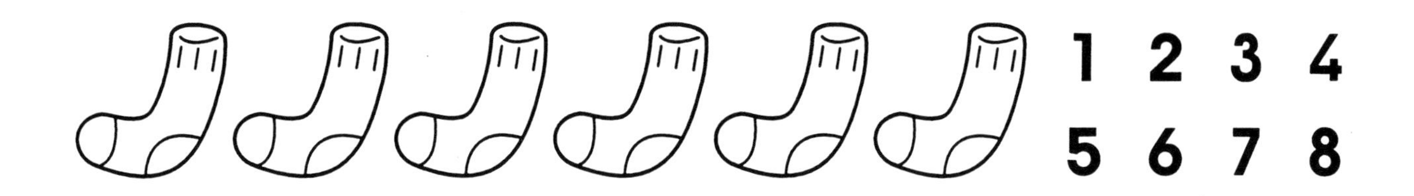

1 2 3 4
5 6 7 8

---

1 2 3 4
5 6 7 8

1 2 3 4
5 6 7 8

---

1 2 3 4
5 6 7 8

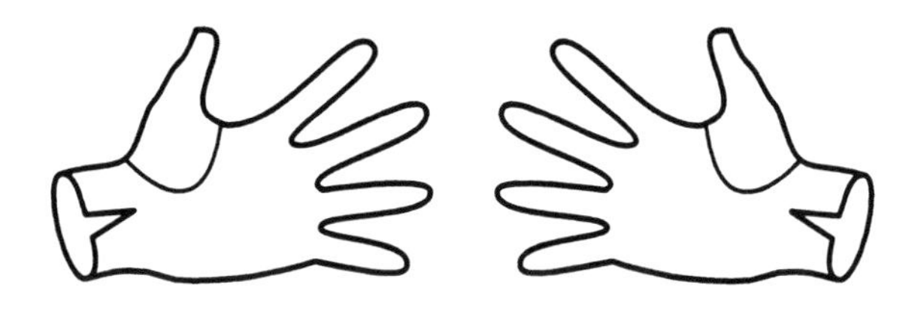

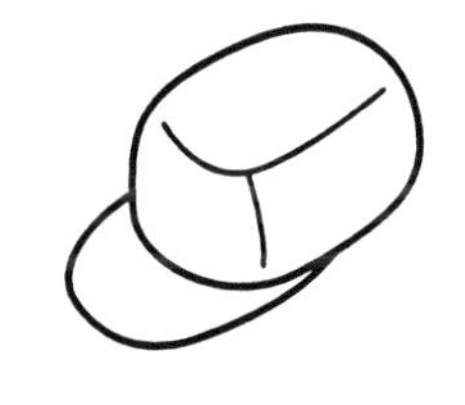

1 2 3 4
5 6 7 8

---

1 2 3 4
5 6 7 8

1 2 3 4
5 6 7 8

Circle the number that is the same.

1	2	4	1	3	8
9	8	3	4	2	9
6	6	4	1	5	3
3	5	1	3	9	10
7	6	7	2	1	5
4	4	9	8	3	2
2	4	1	5	8	2
5	5	4	7	9	3
8	7	8	1	2	5

Numbers 1 to 10

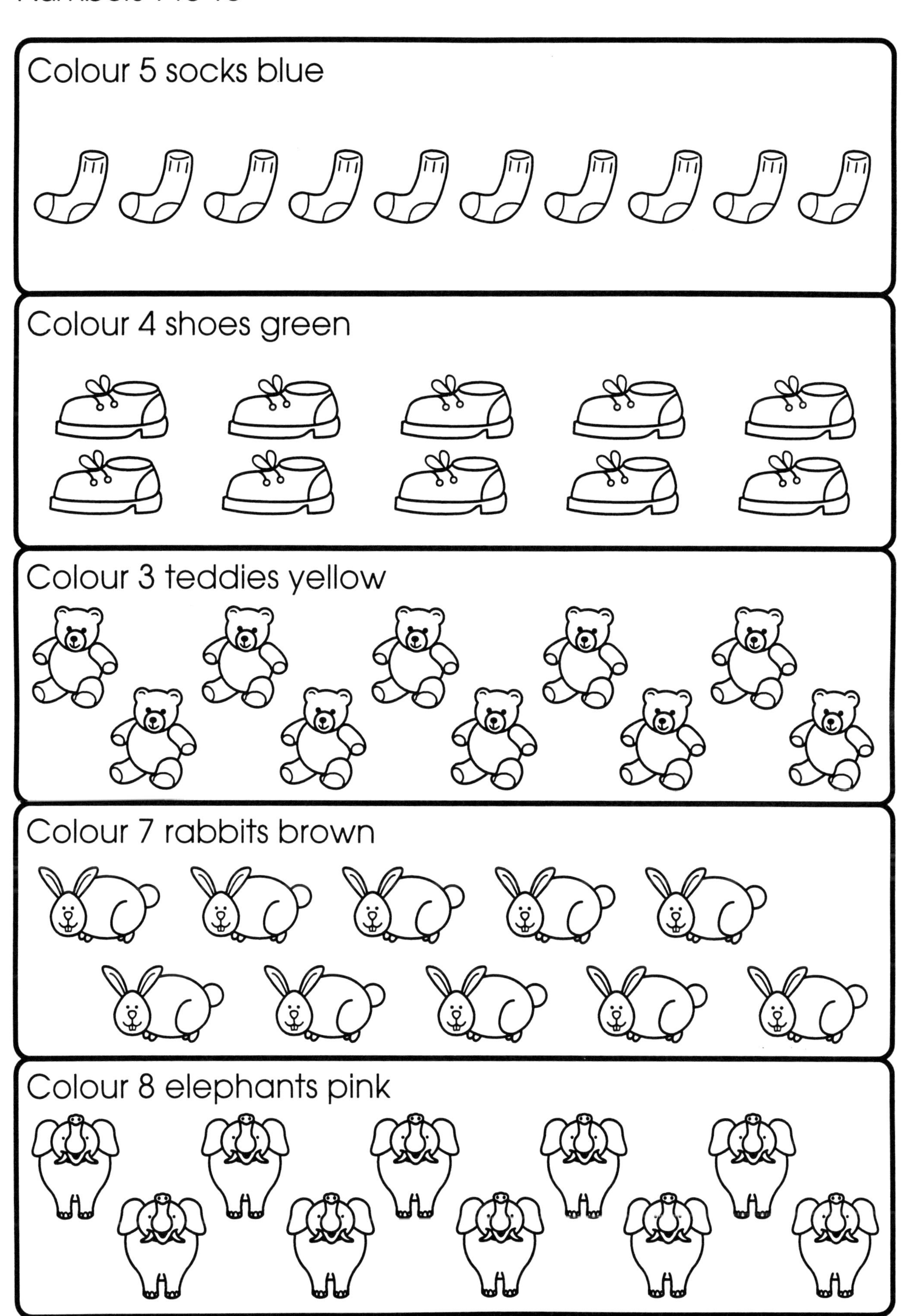

Sets

Colour sets of 4 green. Colour sets of 6 blue.

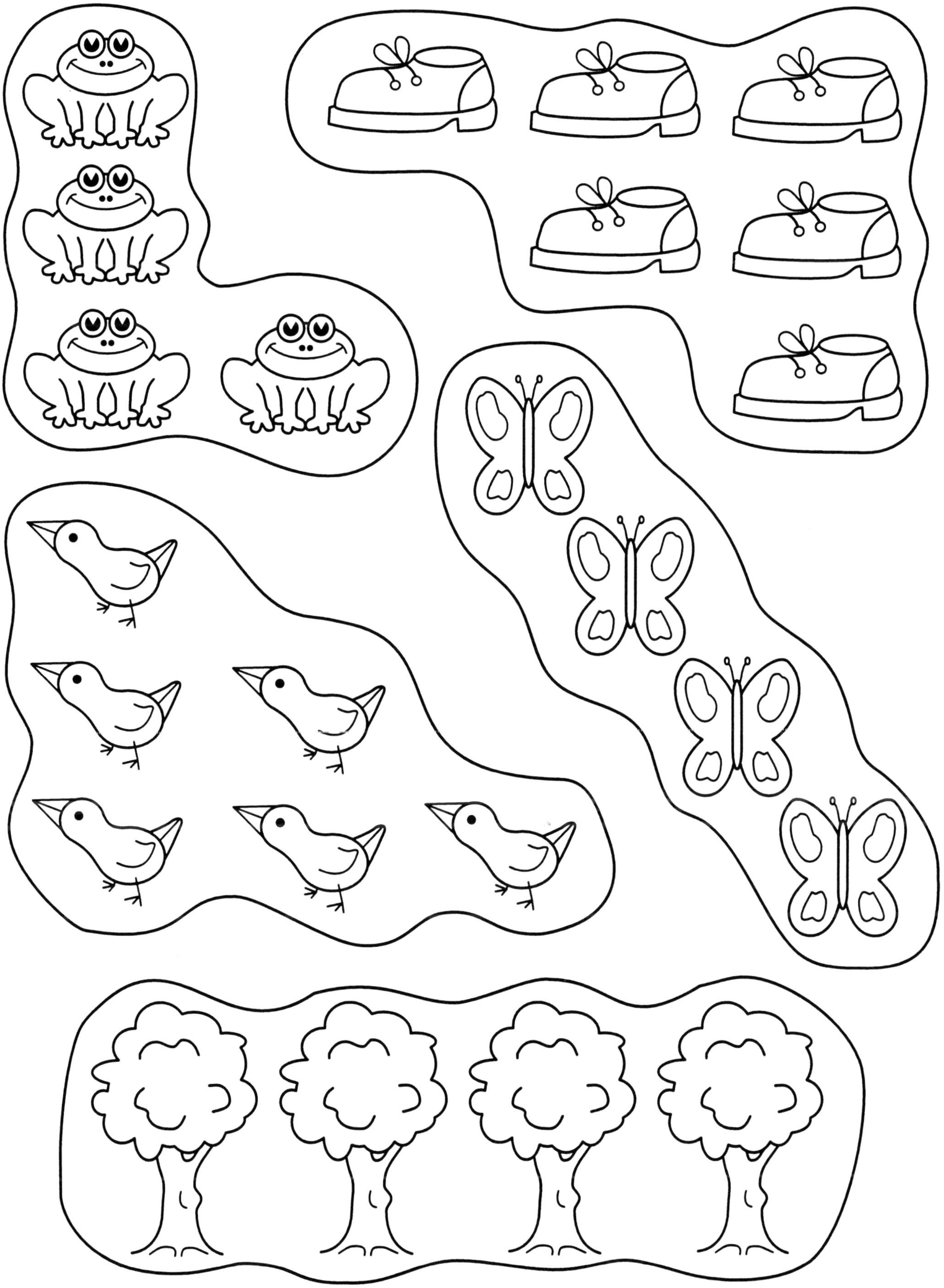

Join the dots.

Join the dots in these pictures.

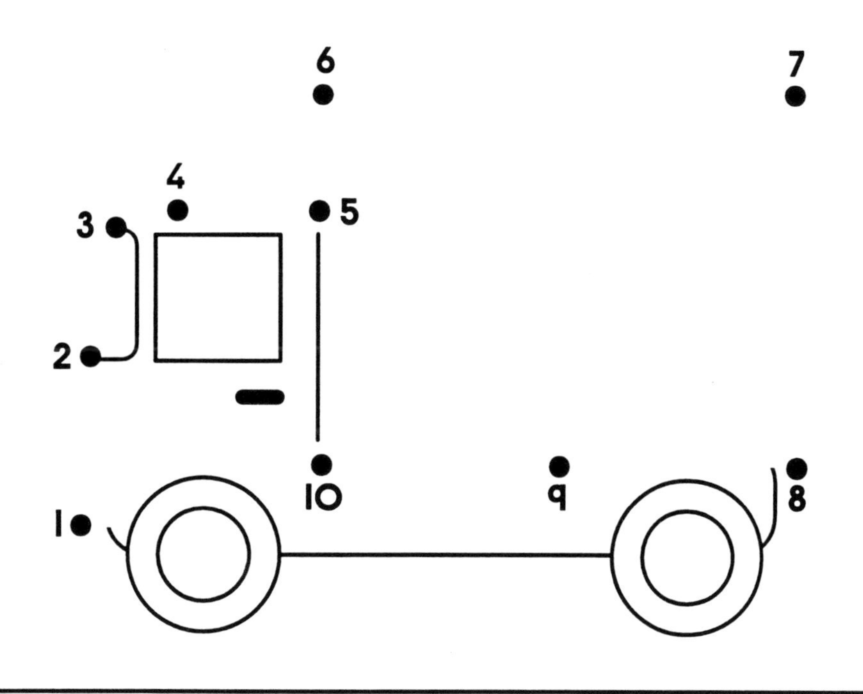

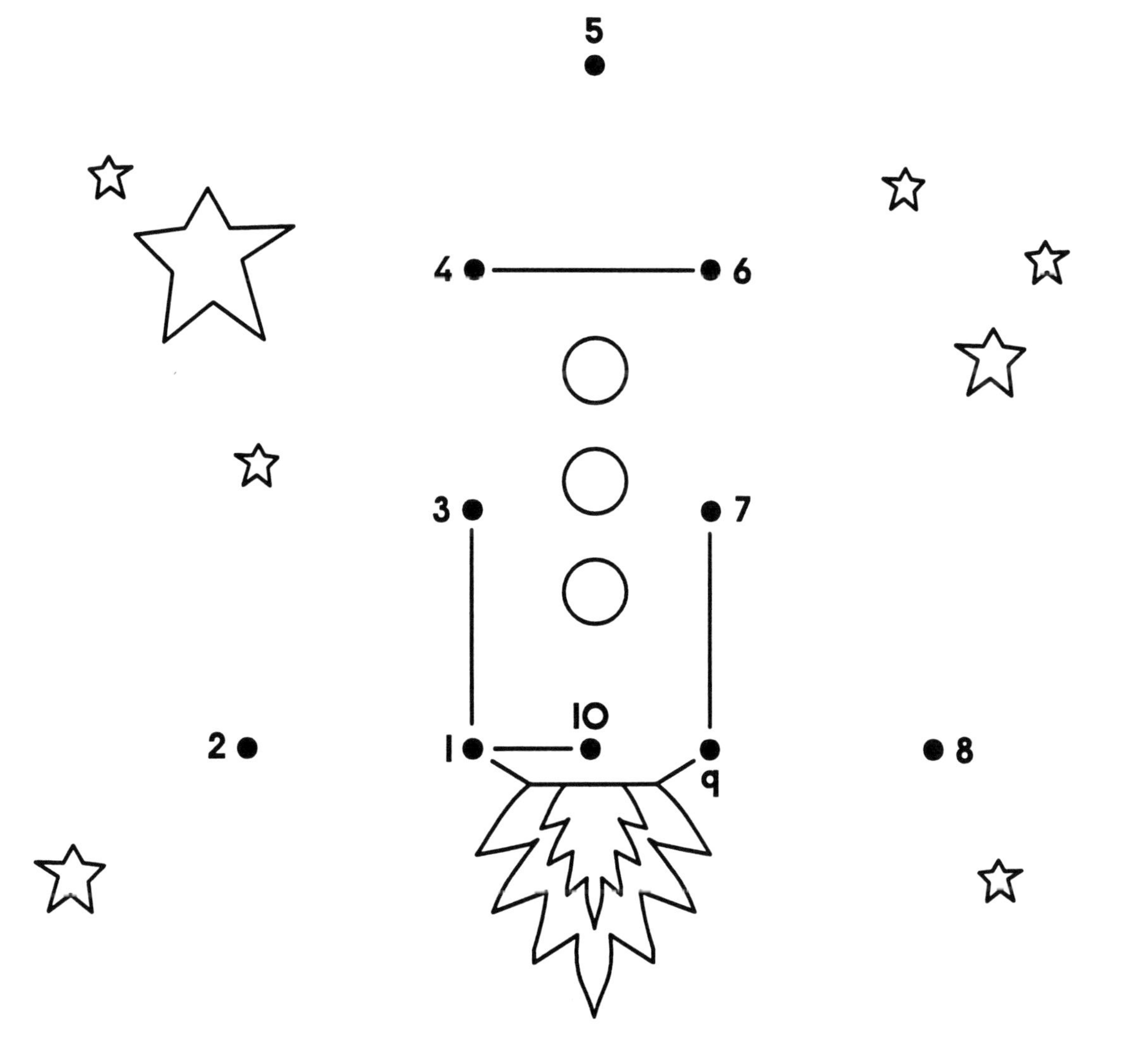

Colour the cats. Cut out the cats.
Paste the cats in the baskets.

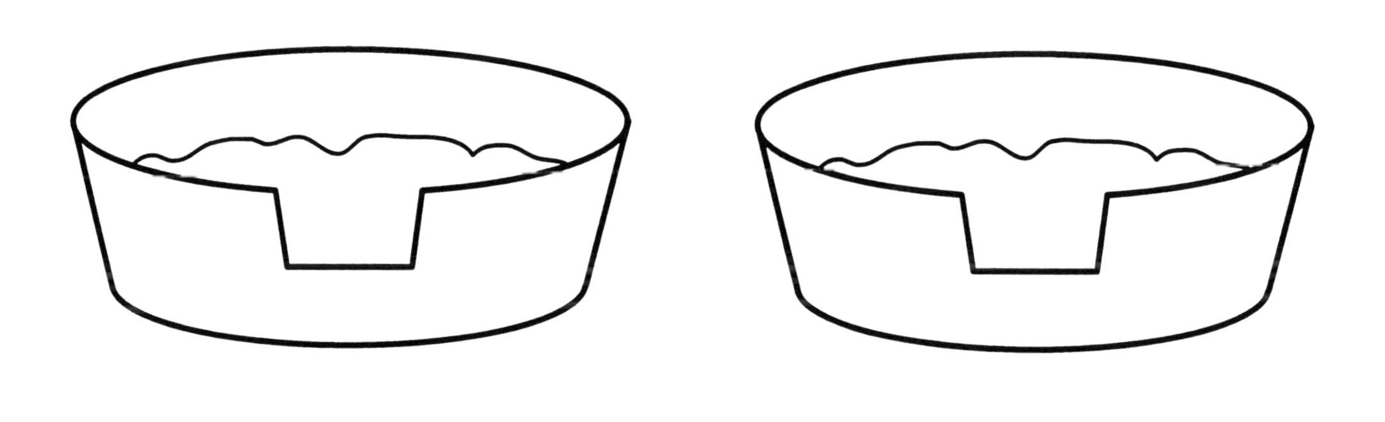

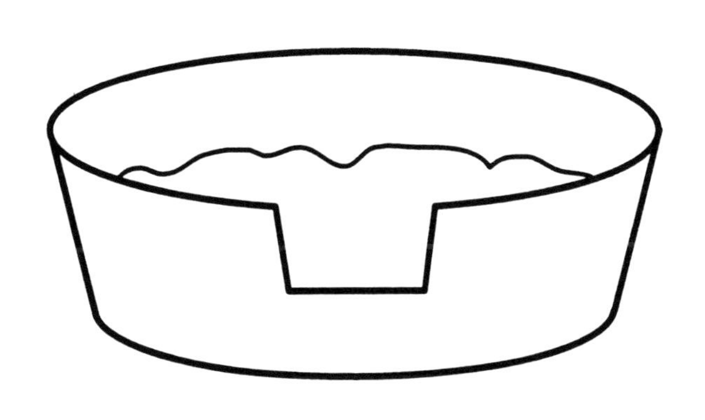

6 Colour the cars. Cut out the cars.
Paste the cars in the parking spaces.

Colour the fish. Cut out the fish.
Paste the fish in the bowls.

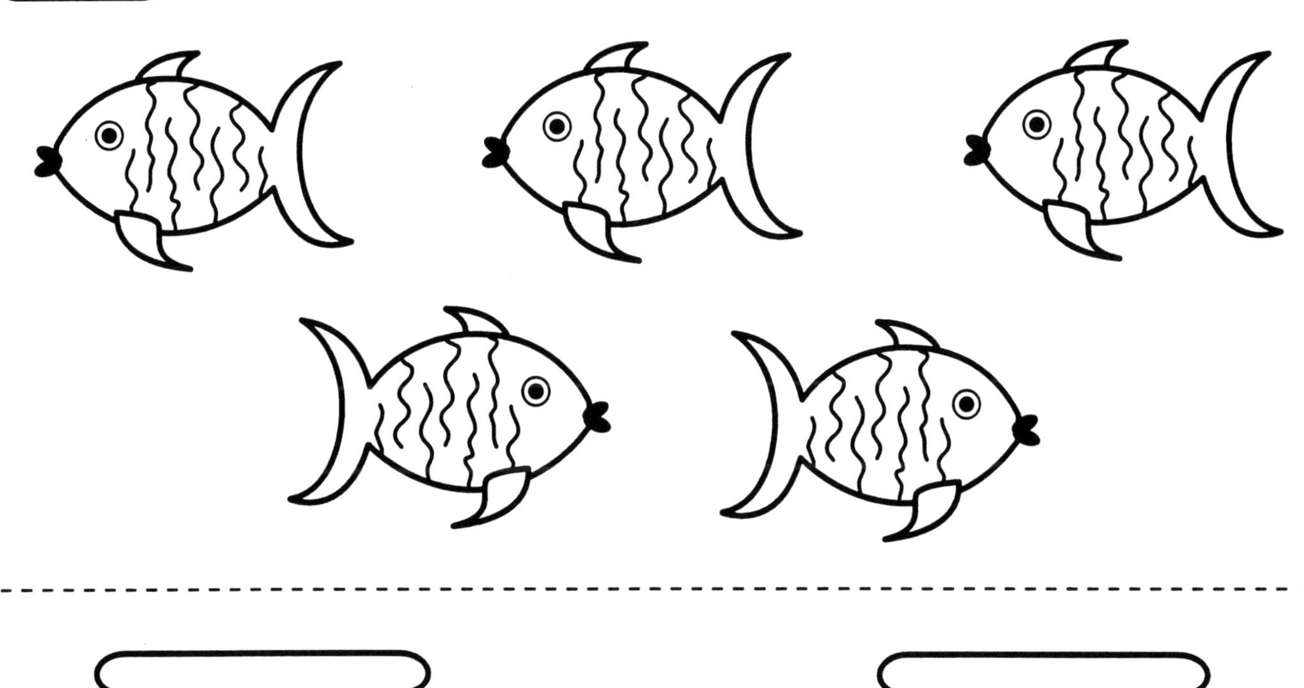

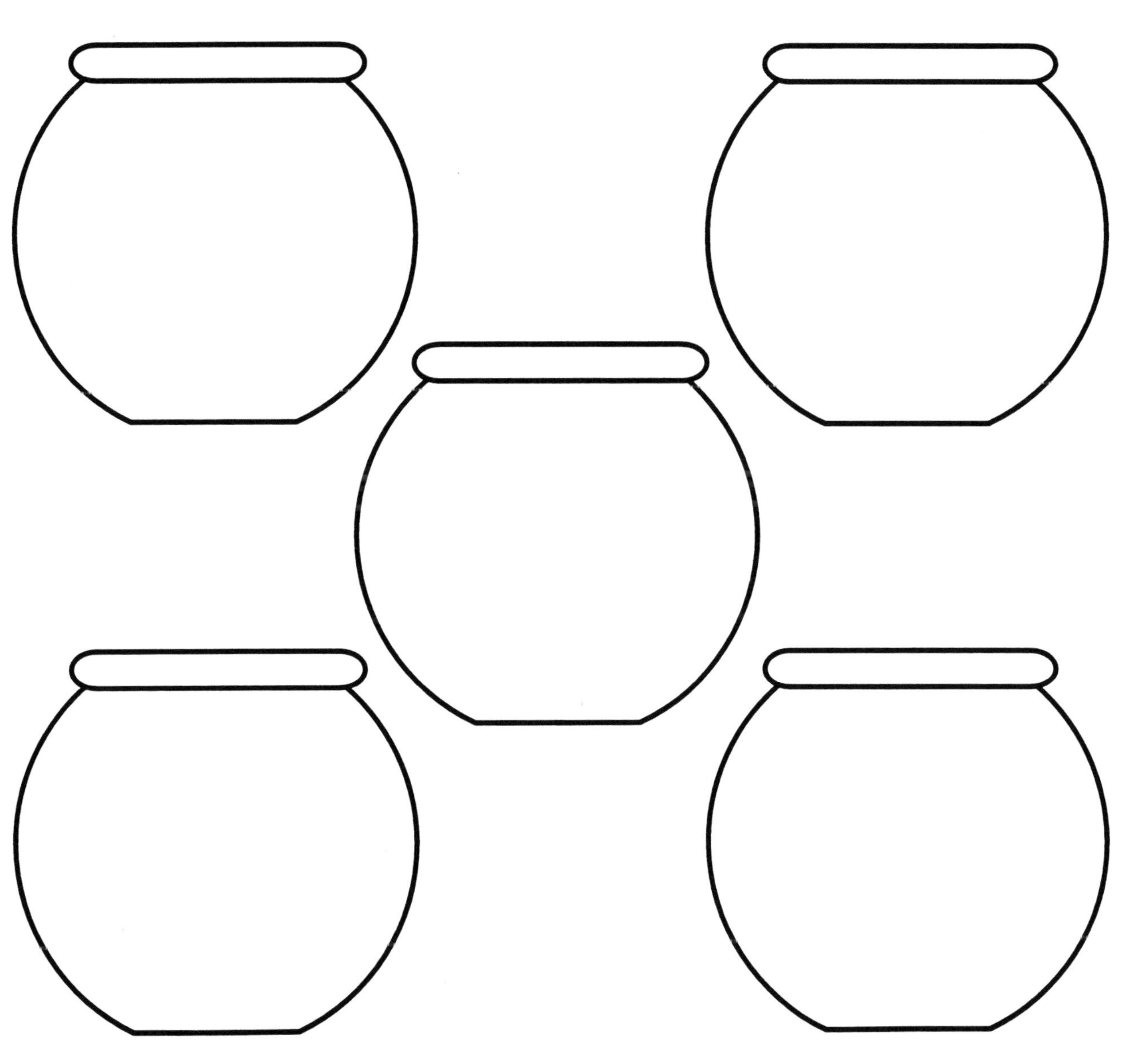

Draw a tail for each cat.

Draw an egg in each cup.

Draw a string for each balloon.

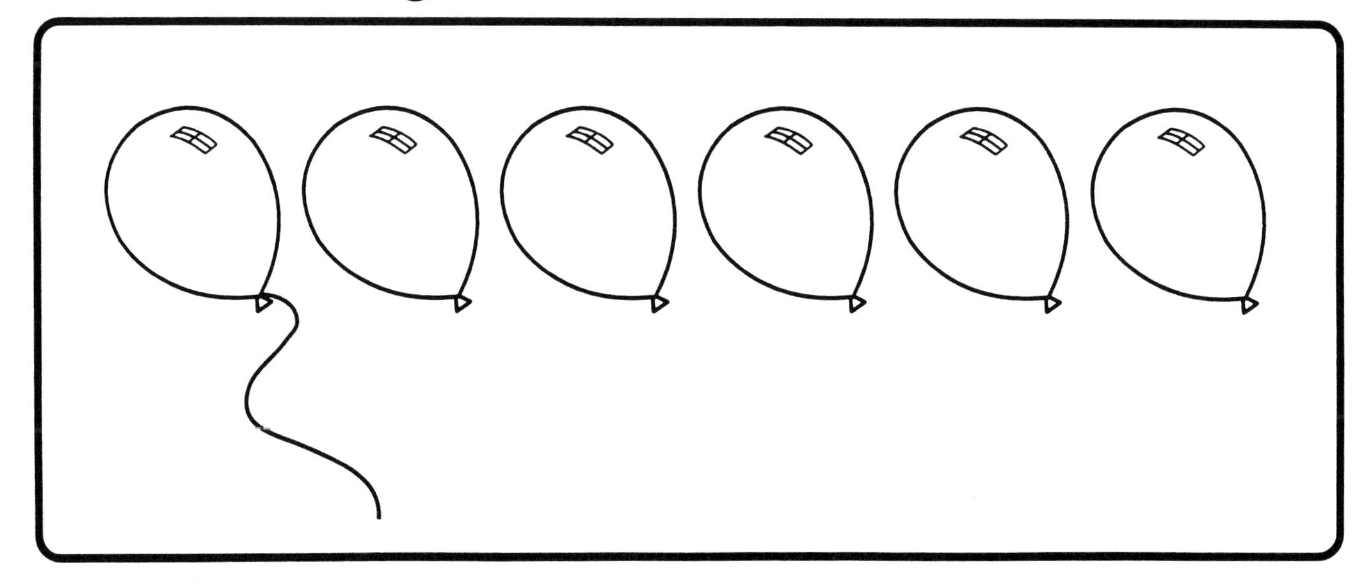

Number Rhymes

Three blind mice

How many mice are there?

Five fat gentlemen standing in a row

How many fat gentlemen are there?

Two little dicky birds

How many dicky birds are there?

Incy Wincy Spider

Join the dots to make the spider's legs.

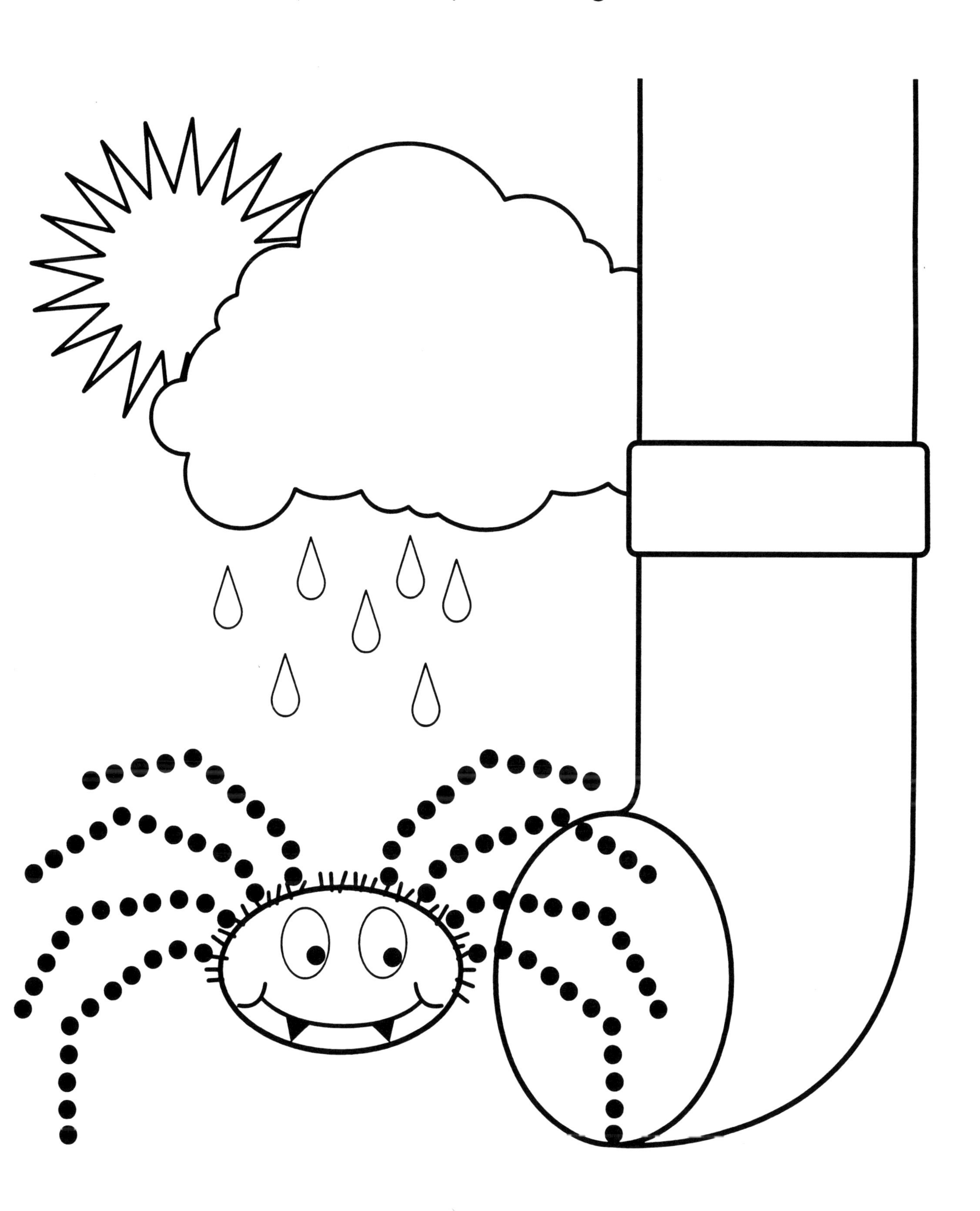

Mary Mary Quite Contrary

Join the dots to make the watering can.

Hickory dickory dock.

Draw the mouse running up the clock, colour the picture.

Humpty Dumpty

Cut and paste Humpty to show what happened.

Goldilocks and the Three Bears

Colour the pictures and cut them out.
Put them in order to tell the story.

Little Red Riding Hood .

Colour the pictures and cut them out.
Put them in order to tell the story.

Three little pigs.

Colour the pictures and cut them out.
Put them in order to tell the story.

The cat

Say what is happening in this picture.
Colour the picture and give it a title.
Name the cat and the people in the picture.

Matching.

Old Macdonald

Make the same sounds as these animals.

Hey Diddle Diddle

Make a jigsaw out of this picture.

Memory time

Look at the objects below then cover them with a piece of paper. How many can you remember?

Try again. Can you remember more this time?

What's missing ?

Look at these pictures and draw the parts that are missing.

I'm a little teapot

Draw a circle around the teapots which are the same.

a
apple
a
a

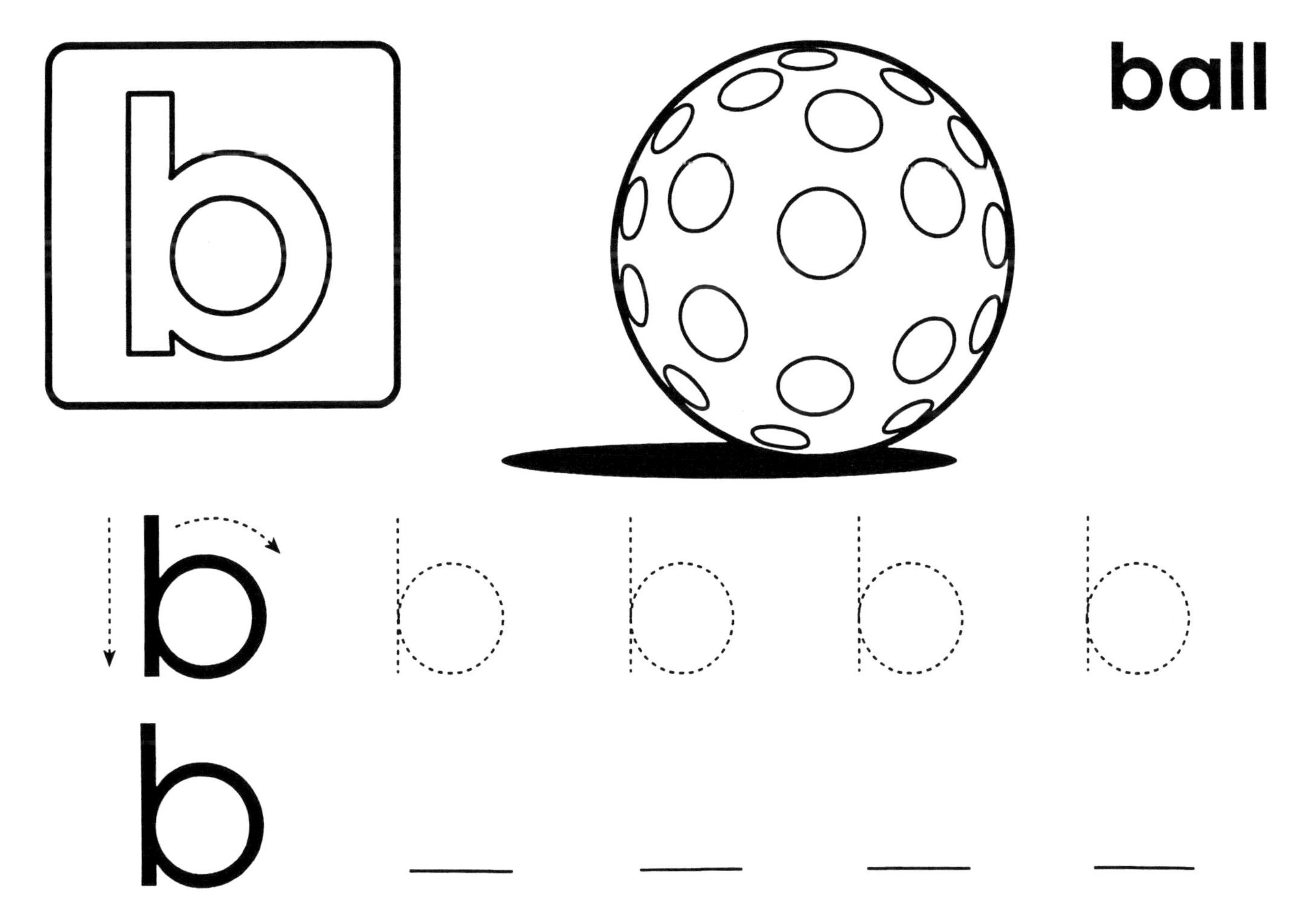
b
ball
b
b

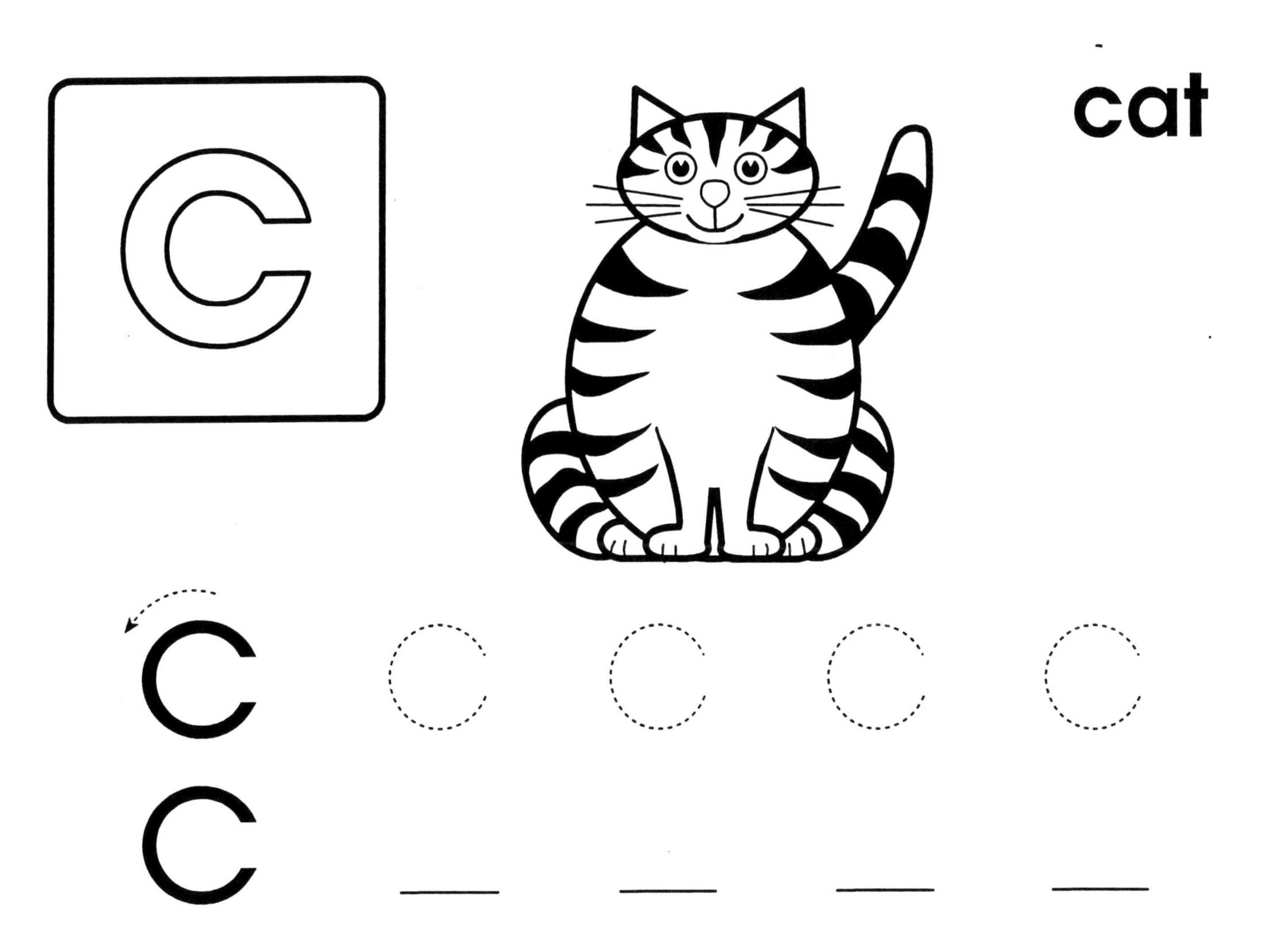
c
cat
c
c

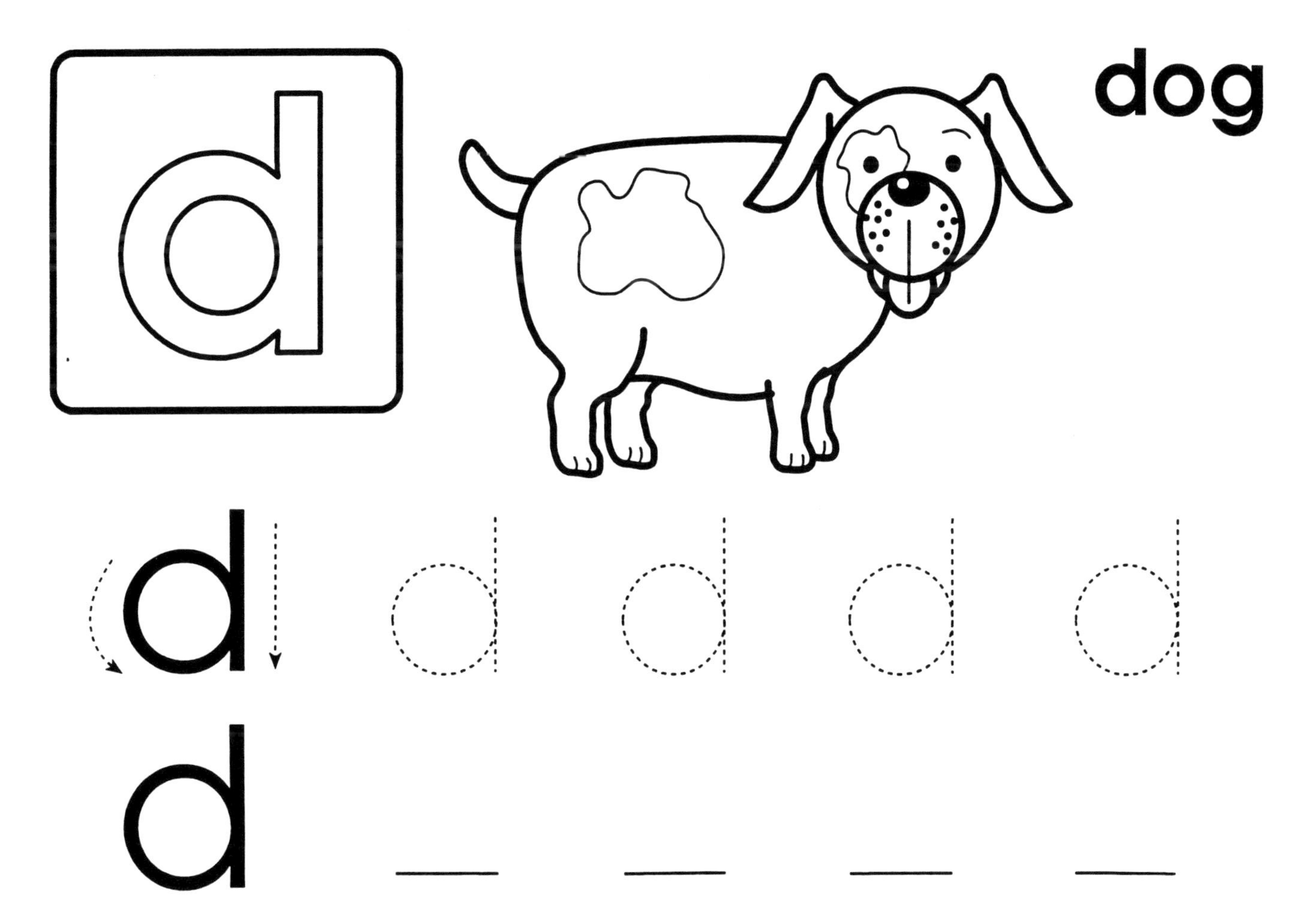
d
dog
d
d

e
elephant
e
e

f
fish
f
f

g
goat
g g g g g
g

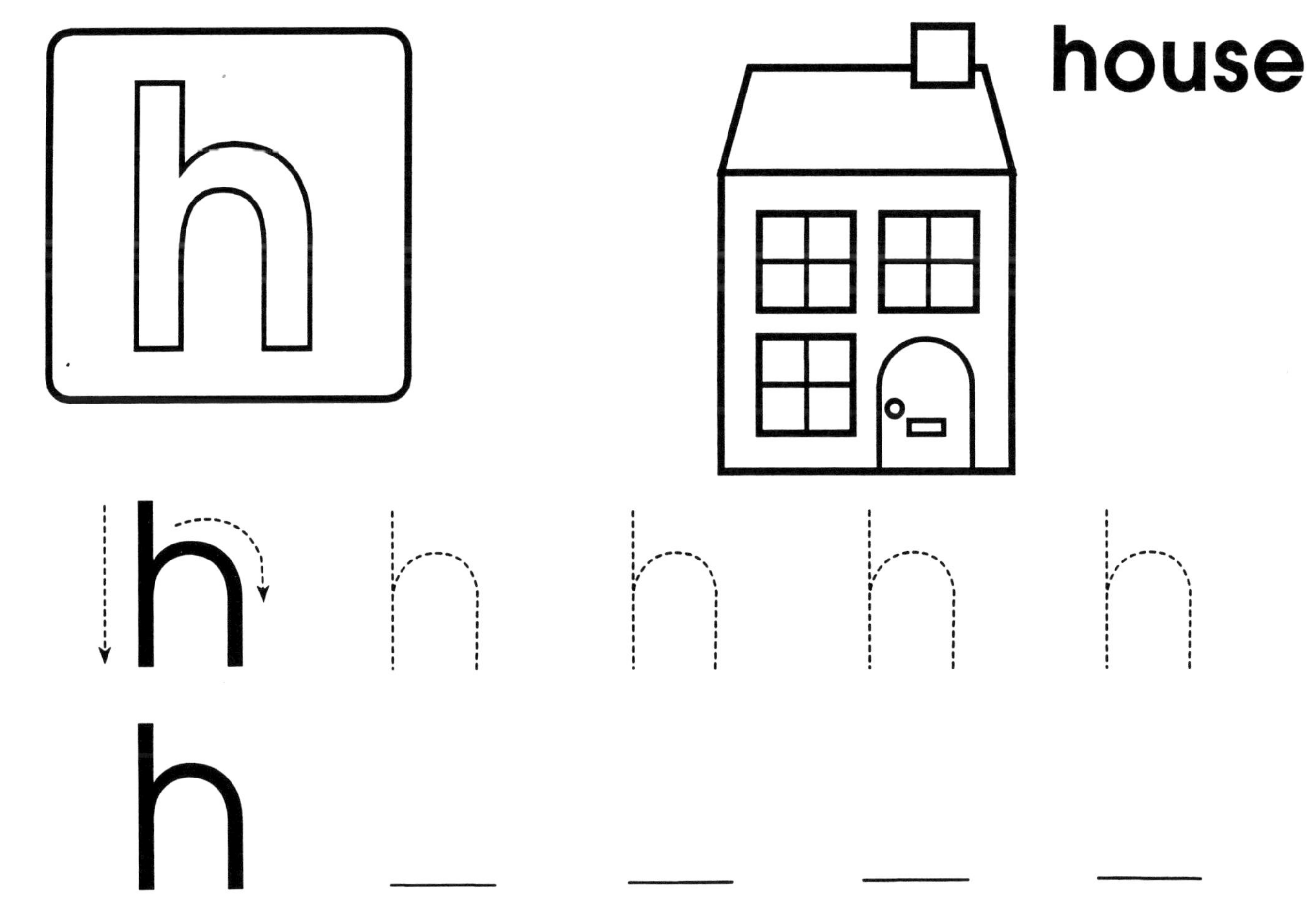
h
house
h h h h h
h

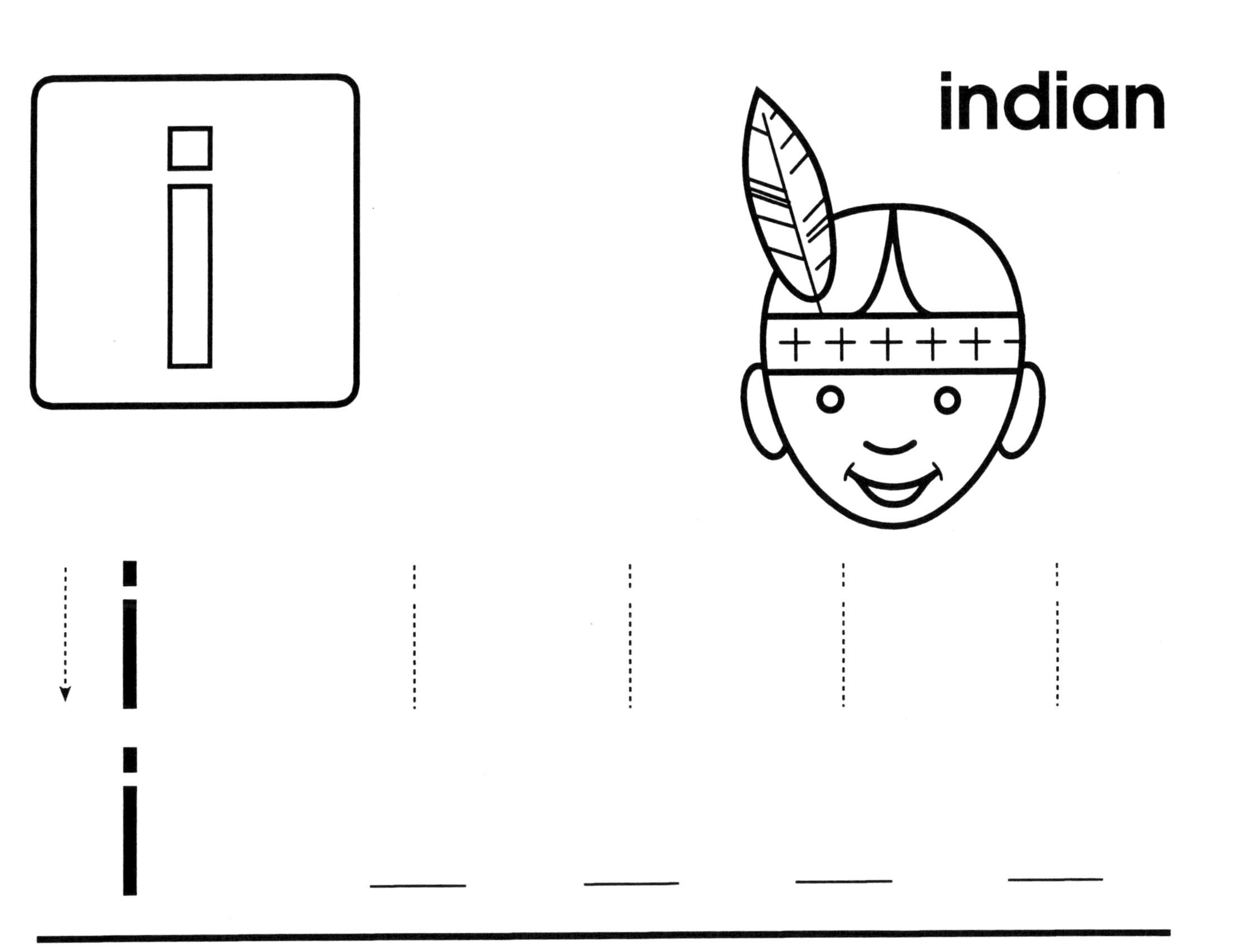
i
indian
i
i

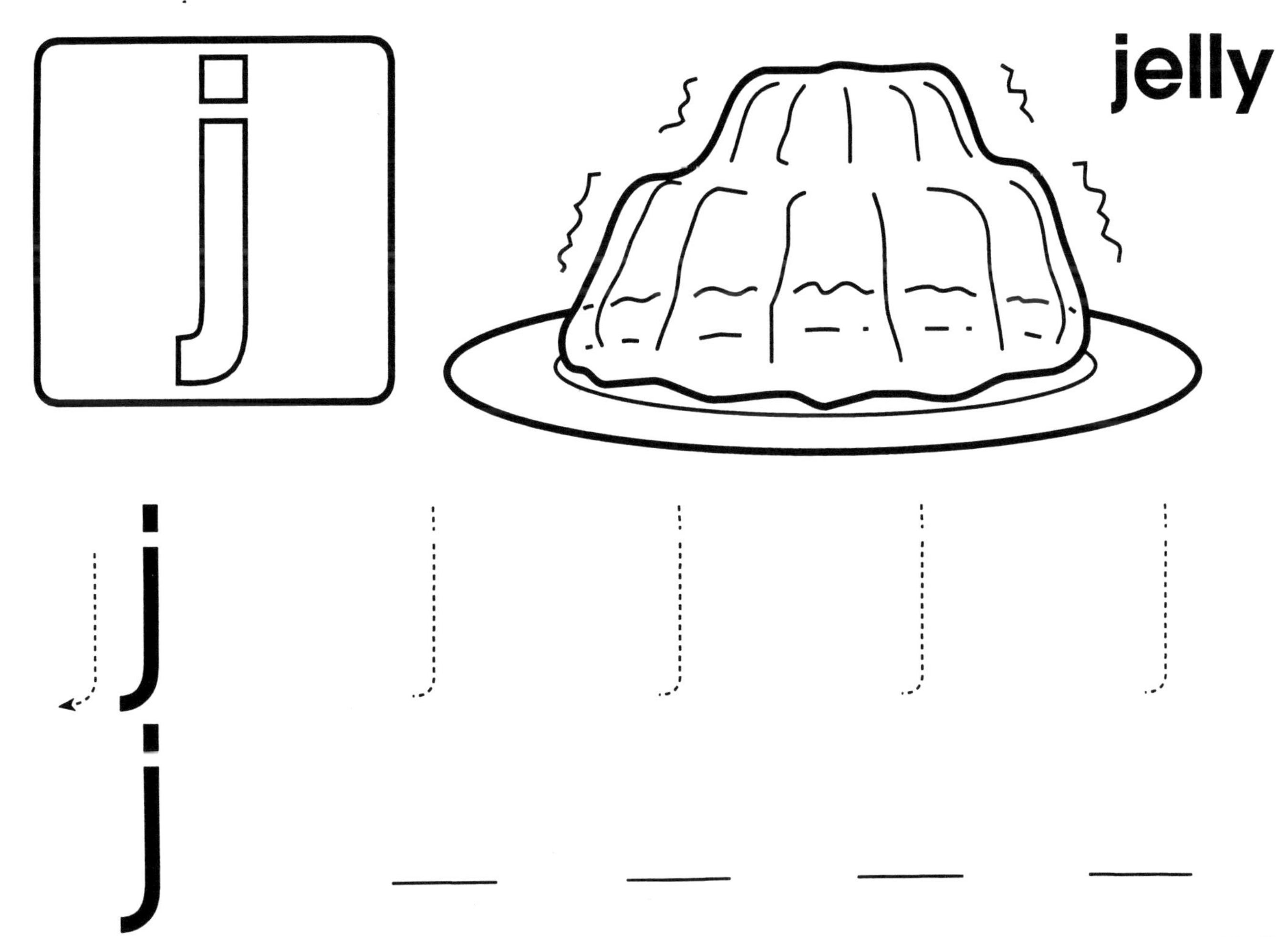
j
jelly
j
j

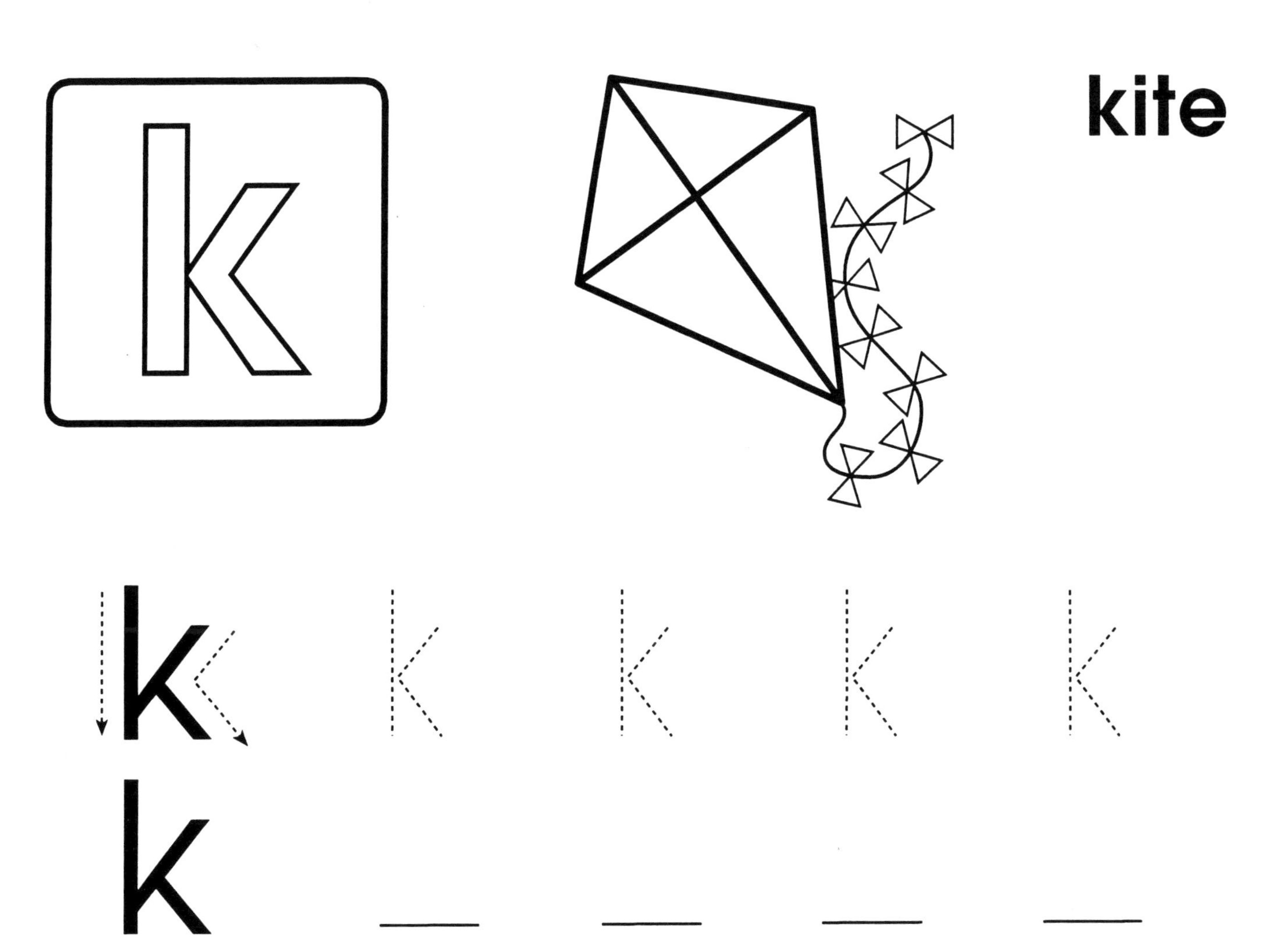
k
kite
k
k

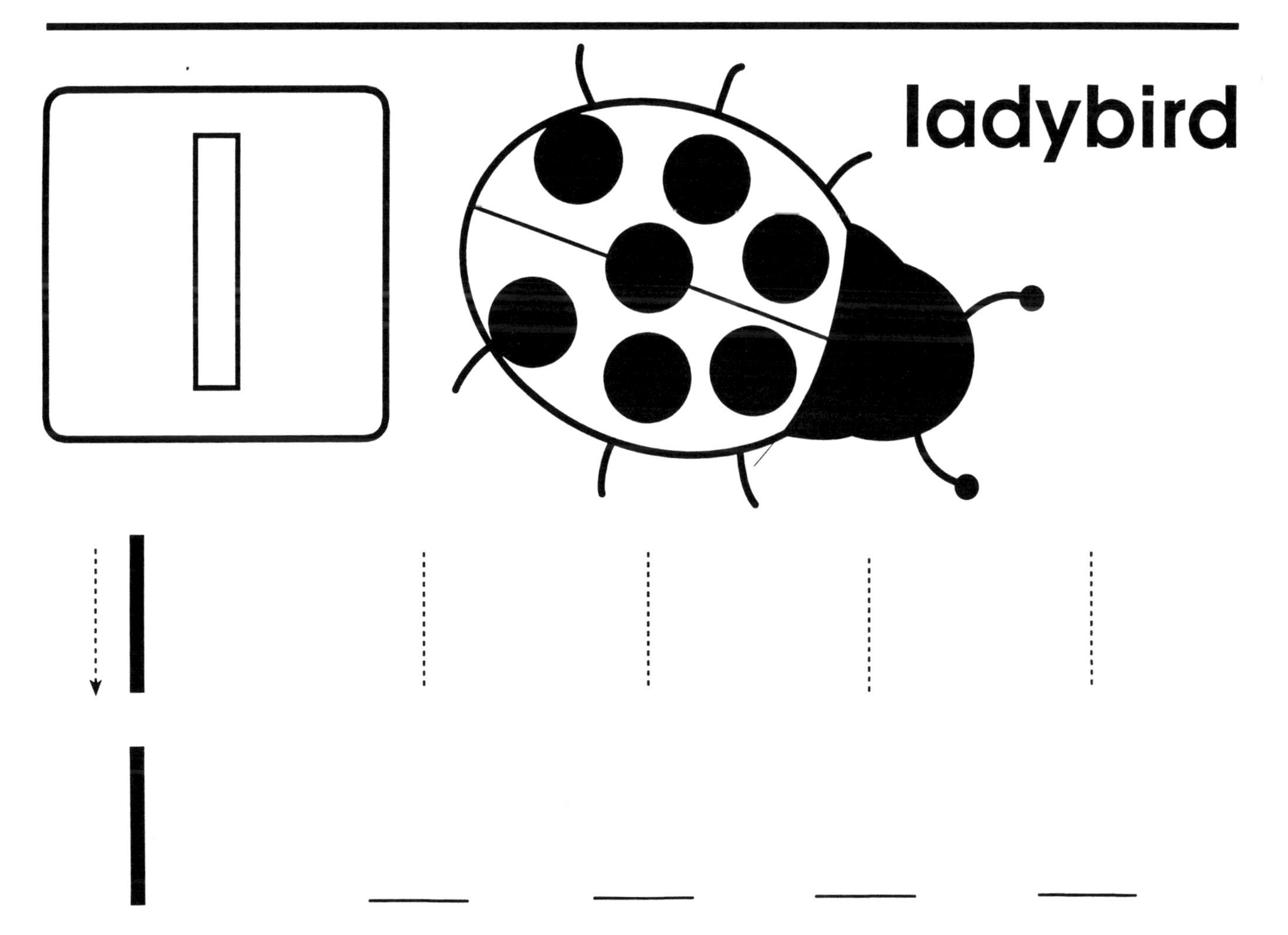
l
ladybird
l
l

m
monkey
m
m

n
nurse
n
n

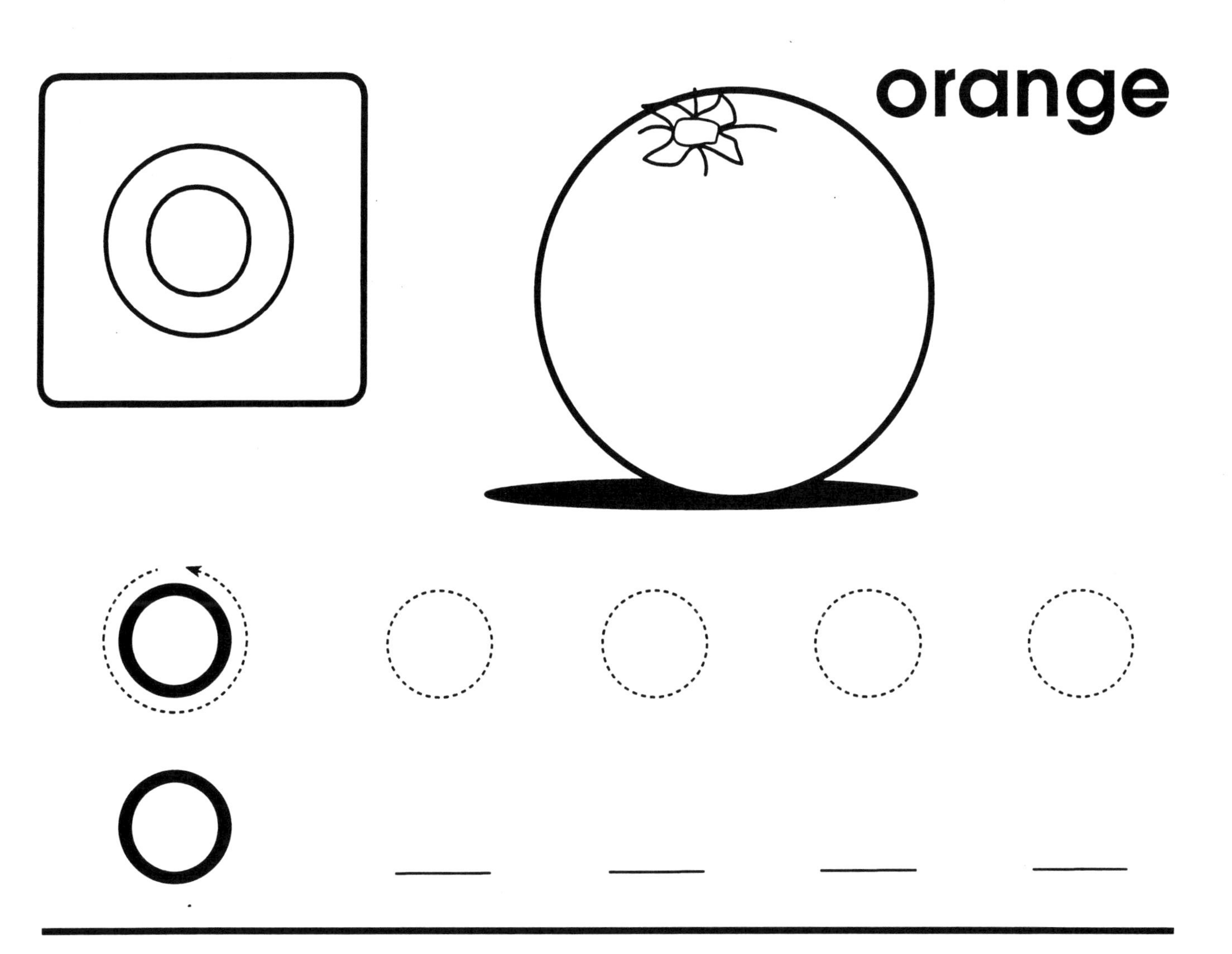
o
orange
o
o

p
penguin
p
p

q
queen
q
q

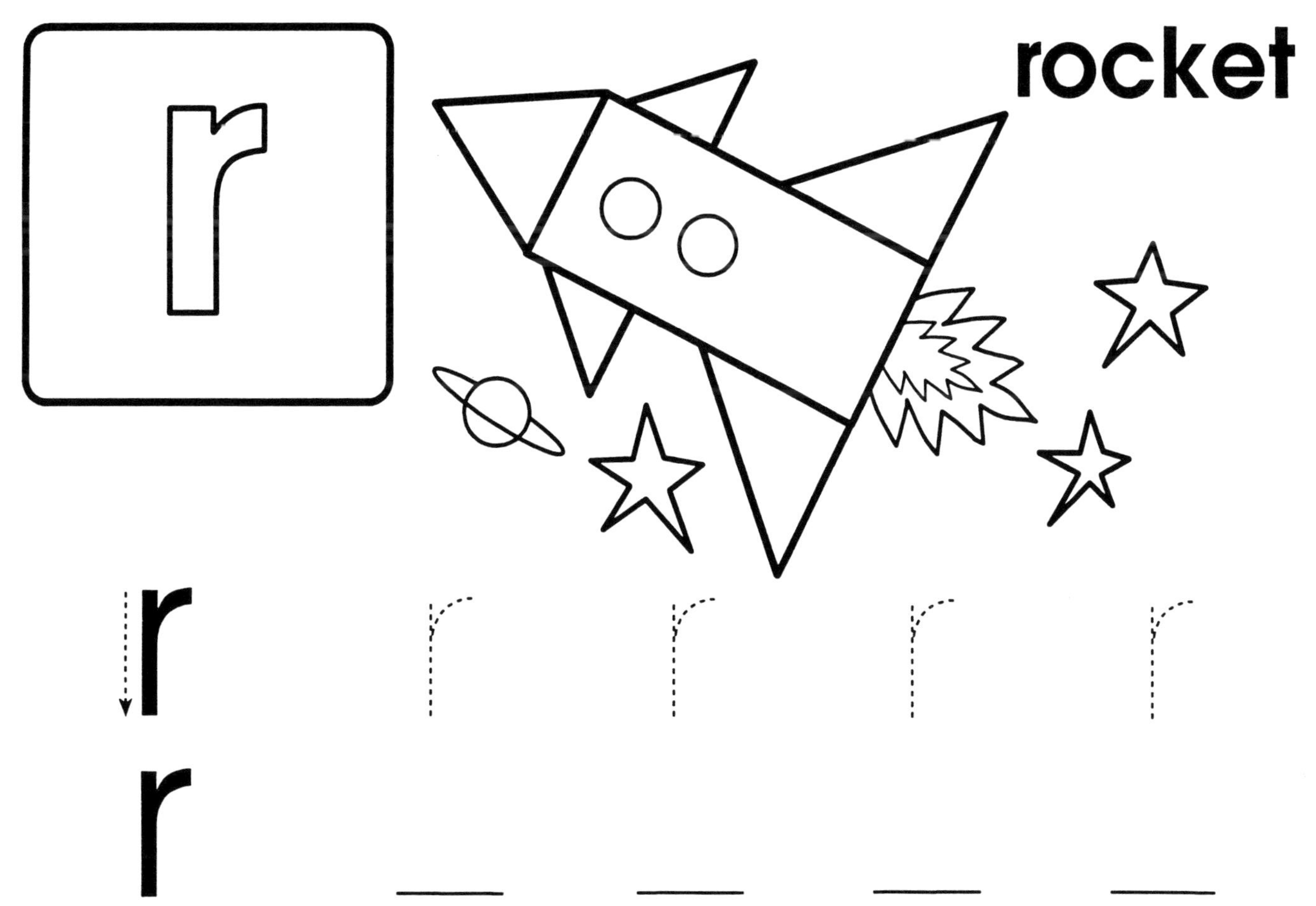
r
rocket
r
r

s
snake
s
s

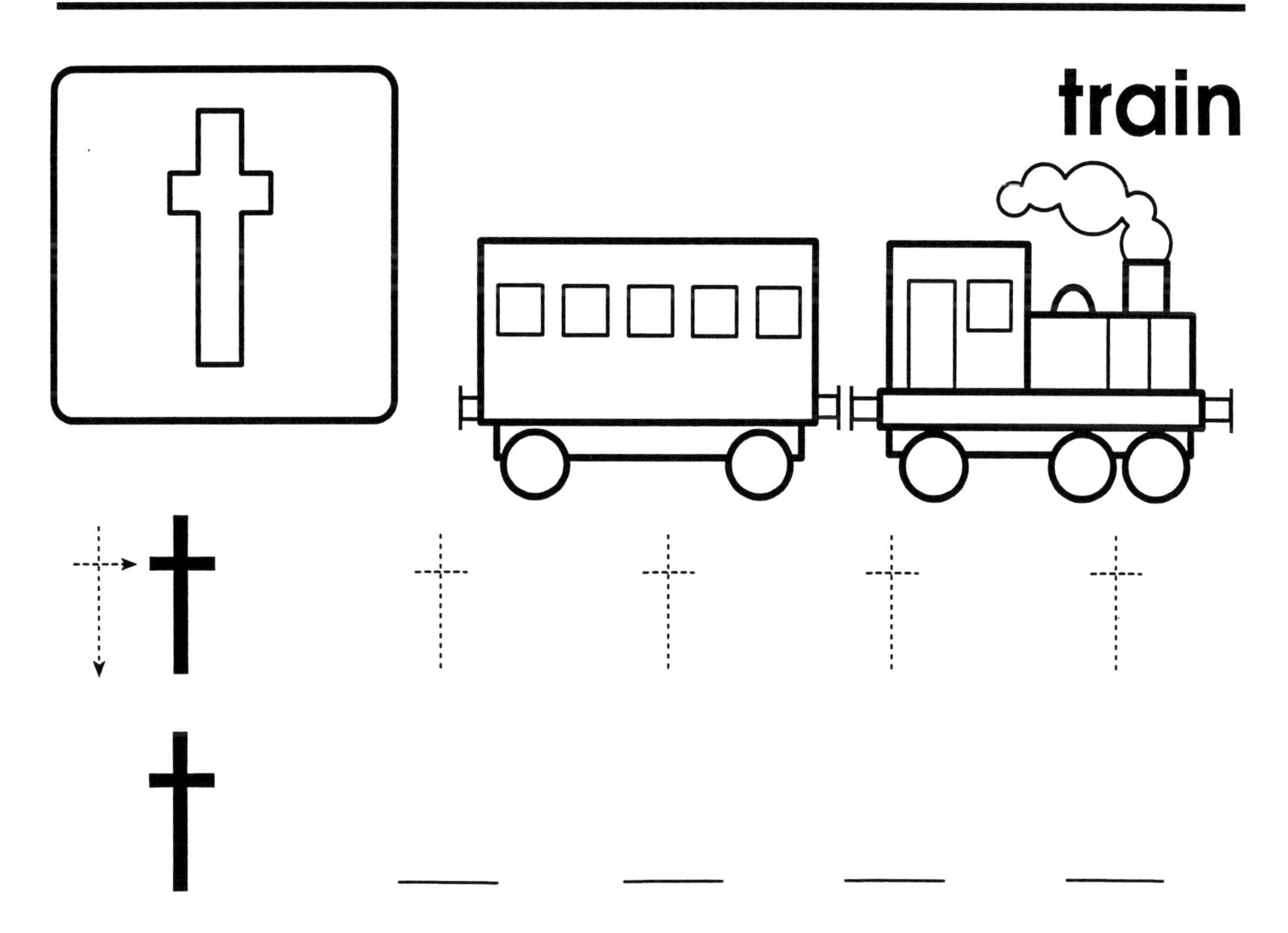
t
train
t
t

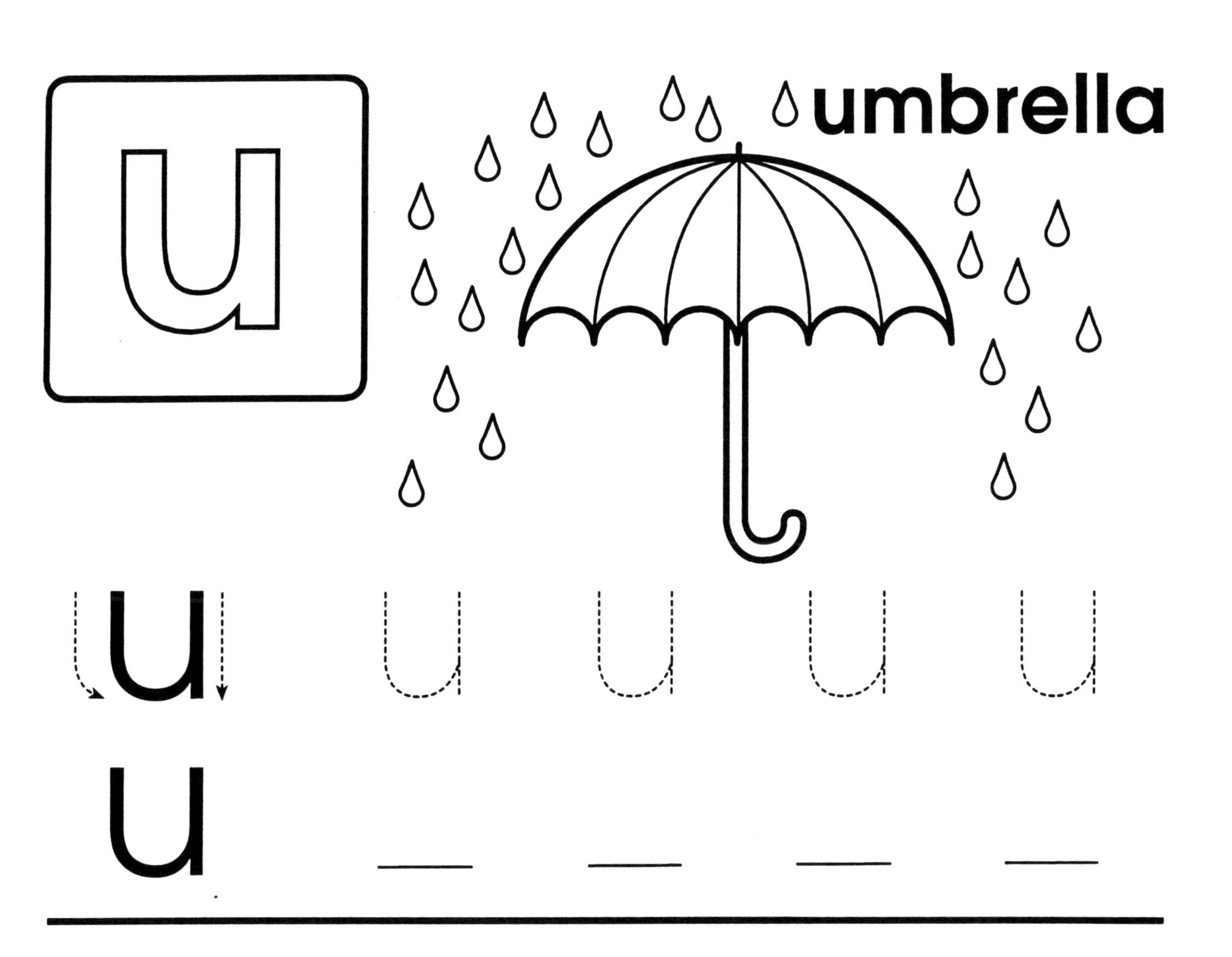

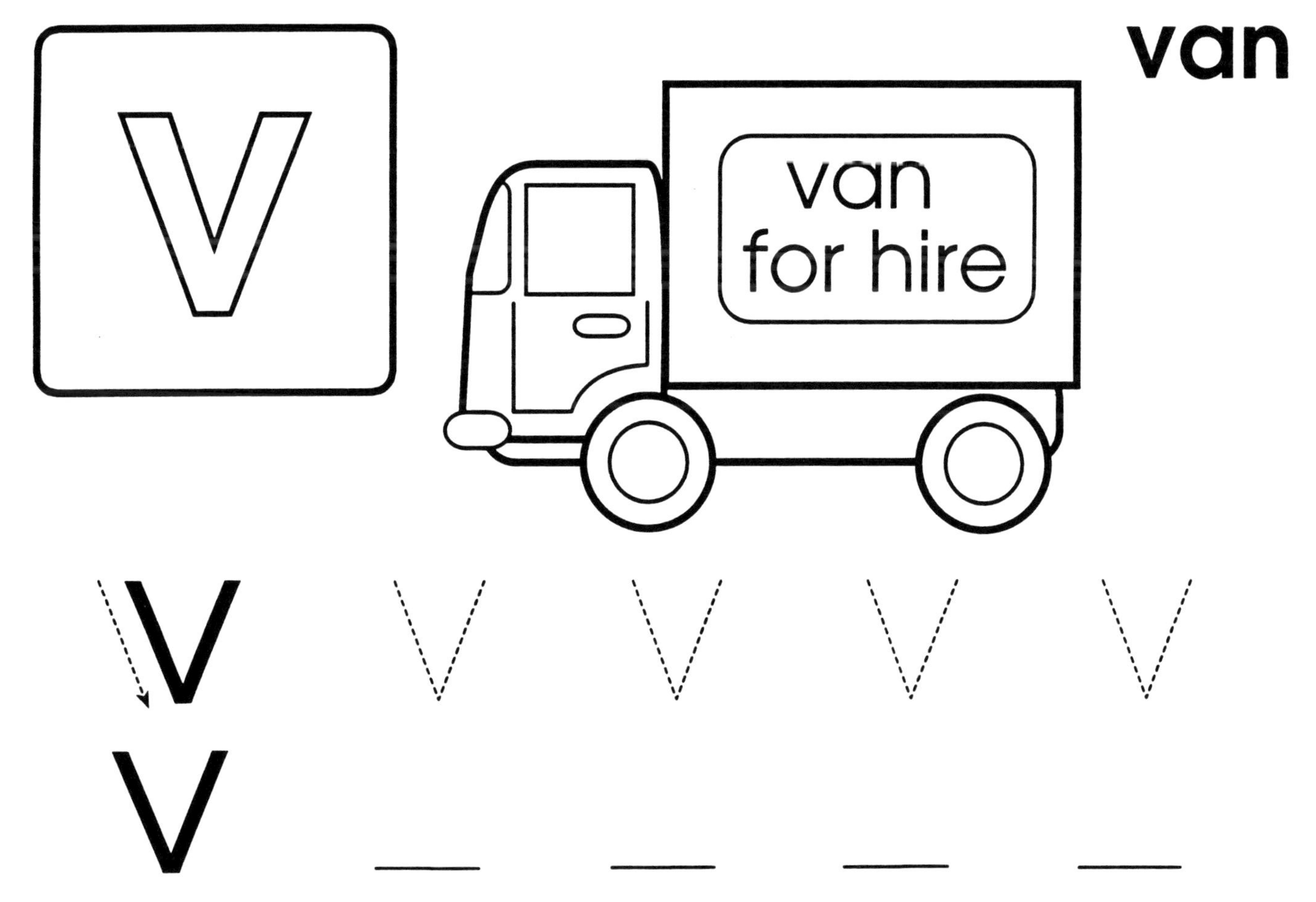

v v v v v

v

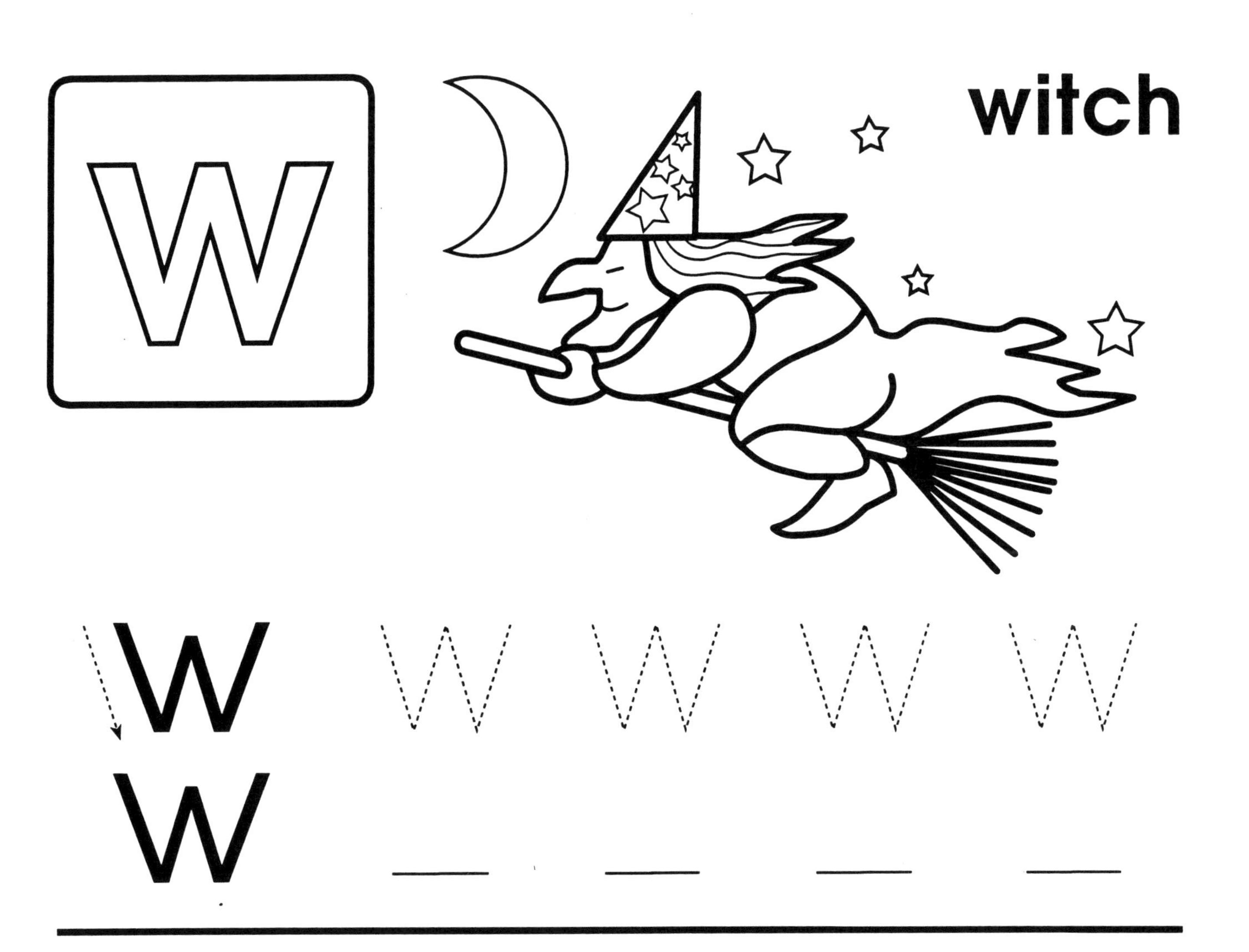

W w w w w

W w ___ ___ ___ ___

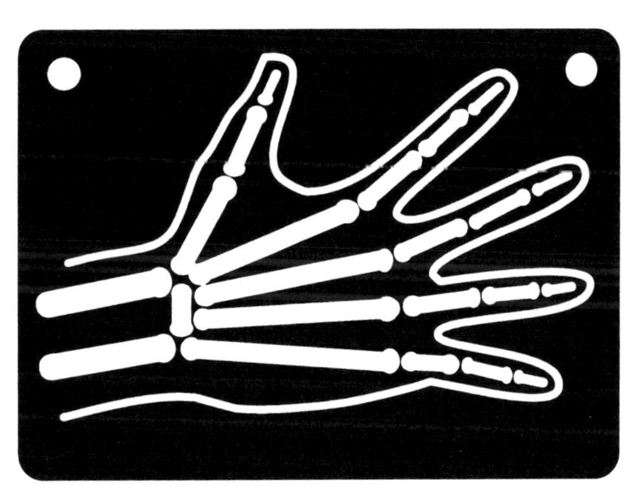

x-ray

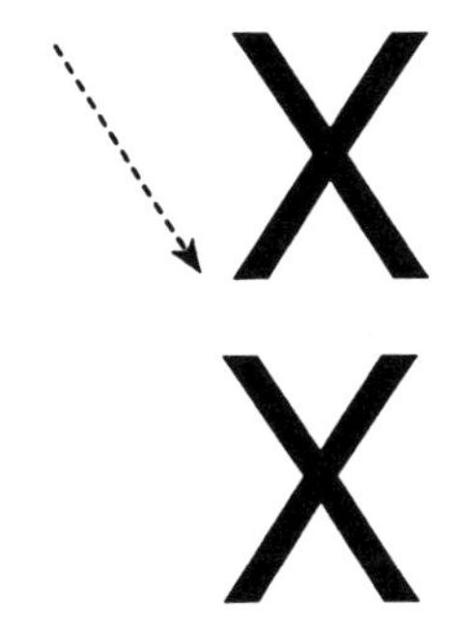

___  ___ 

y
yo-yo
y
y

z
zebra
z
z

a	b	c	d
e	f	g	h
i	j	k	l
m	n	o	p
q	r	s	t
u	v	w	x
y	z		

MASTER FILES
ORDER FORM

KEY STAGE 1 (Age 5 - 7) KEY STAGE 2 (Age 7 - 11) KEY STAGE 3 (Age 11 - 14)

Quantity	Title	ISBN	Price	Cost
	MATHEMATICS (KS1)	1 85772 107 1	£20.00	£
	HISTORY (KS1)	1 85772 112 8	£20.00	£
	ENGLISH (KS1)	1 85772 111 X	£20.00	£
	SCIENCE (KS1)	1 85772 108 X	£20.00	£
	MATHEMATICS (KS2)	1 85772 086 5	£20.00	£
	ENGLISH (KS2)	1 85772 085 7	£20.00	£
	SCIENCE (KS2)	1 85772 087 3	£20.00	£
	MATHEMATICS (KS3)	1 85772 126 8	£20.00	£
	ENGLISH (KS3)	1 85772 127 6	£20.00	£
	SCIENCE (KS3)	1 85772 128 4	£20.00	£
	HISTORY			
	Invaders and Settlers - The Celts (KS2)	1 85772 067 9	£15.95	£
	Invaders and Settlers - The Romans (KS2)	1 85772 070 9	£15.95	£
	Invaders and Settlers - Anglo-Saxons (KS2)	1 85772 068 7	£15.95	£
	Invaders and Settlers - The Vikings (KS2)	1 85772 069 5	£15.95	£
	Life in Tudor Times (KS2)	1 85772 076 8	£15.95	£
	Victorian Britain (KS2 - KS3)	1 85772 077 6	£15.95	£
	The Second World War (KS2 - KS3)	1 85772 121 7	£15.95	£
	The Twentieth Century World (KS2 - KS3)	1 85772 074 1	£15.95	£
	TOPICS			
	Castles (KS2 - KS3)	1 85772 075 X	£15.95	£
	Christmas (Ages 5 - 12)	1 85772 065 2	£20.00	£
	NEW FOR NURSERY CLASSES			
	First Steps (Basic Activities in the 3Rs)	1 85772 130 6	£12.50	£

Total **£** ____________

Name/Organisation/School

Address

Post Code Tel.

Contact Signature

Order Number Date

Available from Foyles Bookshop, Welsh Books Council, Blackwells, Georges, Bookland, Dillons, Hammicks, Waterstones, WH Smith and all good booksellers or direct from

DOMINO BOOKS (WALES) LTD, P O BOX 32, SWANSEA SA1 1FN
TEL. 01792 459378 FAX. 01792 466337

All official orders must have an official requisition form attached (schools, educational establishments, LEAs, bookshops, libraries). Cheques with private orders please.